Volcanoes
NEW AND OLD

SATIS N. COLEMAN

Volcanoes

NEW AND OLD

WITH 97 ILLUSTRATIONS AND TWO MAPS

THE JOHN DAY COMPANY · NEW YORK

COPYRIGHT, 1946, BY SATIS N. COLEMAN

All rights reserved. This book, or parts thereof, must not be reproduced in any form without permission.

This book is published simultaneously
in the Dominion of Canada by
Longmans, Green & Company, Toronto

Tenth Impression

MANUFACTURED IN THE UNITED STATES OF AMERICA

Foreword

This is not a technical book, nor in any sense a scientific treatment of volcanoes. It is mainly a story book.

A visit to the new volcano, Parícutin, in full action, greatly aroused my curiosity, and stimulated much reading on the subject of volcanoes in general. The interest shown by others—high-school students and adults alike—in the casual discussion of my experiences, and their requests for a nontechnical book that can be easily understood by the layman and student with no scientific background, have led to the writing of this book.

The dramas that volcanoes have staged upon our globe have been as interesting, as exciting, and as stimulating as any man-made drama. Volcanoes have played with the emotions of men since the dawn of history—and presumably before—inspiring fear, wonder, confidence, worship, terror, and bewilderment. Bulwer-Lytton recognized this dramatic power when he made use of a volcanic eruption to heighten the climax of his *The Last Days of Pompeii* (although, as is explained on page 176, his story does not conform to the facts of that eruption).

There are probably inaccuracies also in the accounts contained in this book. If so, they are unintentional, for I have tried to adhere to the facts so far as they could be found. My personal experience covers only two active volcanoes—Vesuvius years ago, and Parícutin recently—so it has been necessary to depend on the accounts of others for the stories of other volcanic performances. For some of the greatest of volcanic catastrophies, the records are meager, and doubtless there have been numberless spectacular eruptions with no human witnesses. Indeed, one of the most terrific volcanic explosions of all history took place in Alaska only a few decades ago almost without an audience, and there, as in many places on the globe, the making of records seemed of no importance to the native observers. So inaccuracies are to be expected.

It would be both impossible and purposeless to catalogue all the thousands of volcanic eruptions even of the last twenty centuries, much less those of earlier times. Only some seventy-five or eighty selected ones are discussed here.

Not only do volcanoes provide exciting story material. To many people they are the greatest stimulant to the imagination, and to curiosity and interest in the work of Nature's forces. For, after all, the study of volcanoes is the key to understanding the constitution of our earth; they furnish us our only opportunity to observe the formation of original rock material from the earth's interior; and they also give undoubted evidence of great hidden energy which man must learn either to avoid or to redirect. Therefore, to approach the study of the earth through the direct evidences offered by volcanoes is logical, and a greater interest in geology follows naturally from an interest in the behavior of volcanoes.

Perhaps these pages may stimulate some reader to explore, of his own accord, more deeply into scientific matters; and when interest is once aroused, there is no limit to the paths it may follow in seeking satisfaction. Every educator knows that the development of a "seeking attitude" toward knowledge is much better than merely offering information, and a greater feeder for creative genius. If, therefore, the reading of this book should awaken in a few people a greater interest in the earth and its wonders, and stimulate a greater curiosity concerning the natural laws that control the behavior of things around us, beneath us, and above us, the writing of the book will have been worth while.

SATIS N. COLEMAN

New York City
January 1946

Contents

Volcanoes
NEW AND OLD

Three Lions

CLOUDS OF DUST AND ASHES RISING FROM THE NEWEST VOLCANO ON THE AMERICAN CONTINENT— EL PARÍCUTIN, MEXICO, IN APRIL, 1943.

This photograph was taken from the village of San Juan Parangaricutiro, four miles from the volcano, which was then only two months old.

1:

The Birth of a Volcano

Dionisio Polido's cornfield lay in the pleasant valley of Cuyizirio in the southwestern part of Mexico. It seemed to be especially favored by nature, for the earth was warmer there than anywhere else on the farm. The sun was doing its best for Dionisio's corn patch. For many days he had felt it warm to his bare feet as, with his wooden plow and two oxen, he had plowed his field. Even after sundown the plowed earth was still warm; and when the nights were cold, Dionisio found it more comfortable to sleep on the ground than in his own hut.

One day Dionisio saw what appeared to be a little wisp of smoke coming from a tiny crack in the ground. He supposed that some dry leaves under the soil had caught fire, so he shoveled fresh earth over the spot, in order to put out the fire, and patted it down with his hand. But the smoke came again, and Dionisio was puzzled.

For several days other wisps of smoke appeared, and the earth became even warmer to Dionisio's bare feet. It is said that he went to the neighboring village of San Juan Parangaricutiro (pronounced San Wan Pa-ran-ga-ree-coo-tée-ro) to see the padre, and described to him what had happened in the cornfield. But the padre was incredulous; he thought Dionisio had been drinking too much pulque and had imagined these things, so he sent him back to work on his farm. In a few days Dionisio knelt before the padre again, and told him there were even more smoking cracks in the field, and that the smoke was rising higher and higher. This time the padre followed Dionisio to see this strange thing; and when he saw the jets of smoke spurting up from the soil, the padre, too, was puzzled and uneasy, and said, "Dionisio, we must

1

pray." After their prayers were finished, the padre, greatly bewildered, returned to his church to pray again.

Several days later, at about five o'clock on the afternoon of February 20, as Dionisio leaned against his plow while his oxen were resting, he heard a loud, rumbling sound. The whole earth seemed to tremble. An angry roar came up from beneath the ground and grew louder and louder. More smoke came out and whirled up into the sky. (It appeared as smoke, but doubtless it was steam.) He ran toward the house shouting for his wife to "Come quick! A miracle! A miracle!" But before he and his wife could collect their wits, a great earthquake tore the earth open, while steam and sand, and even large stones from under the soil, came shooting up into the air.

Dionisio and his wife did not wait to see their house and farm covered with fire and brimstone. They ran in terror toward the village of Parícutin, to tell the people what was happening. But the villagers had felt the earthquake, and the road was already filled with panic-stricken people who were fleeing for their lives. Dionisio's friends in Parícutin had seen this monstrous column boiling up into the sky, and in great panic they, too, were gathering their cherished belongings and piling them into carts and on the backs of their burros. The priest was calling for strong men to come and help carry the sacred image of Our Lord of the Miracles to another village for safekeeping.

When darkness came, the whole countryside was lighted by the glowing rocks and cinders that came leaping, like flames, every few seconds from the opening in the earth. The roar of the explosions was like hundreds of cannon being shot at the same time. Great masses of red-hot rock were being hurled eighteen hundred feet into the air, and thunderous explosions caused the earth to heave and surge. The hot rocks that were belched forth fell back and began to pile around the opening.

Thus, on that afternoon of February 20, 1943, a volcano was born, and began at once to build a mountain in a valley where

2

WHEN PARÍCUTIN WAS ONLY ONE DAY OLD.
This volcano is situated in the state of Michoacan, 200 miles in air line due west of Mexico City, in a fertile valley about 7,500 feet above sea level, which means that the climate is always cool. Several hundred volcanic cones, of various ages, stand within a radius of seventy-five miles from the volcano, most of them being "cinder" cones, from 200 to 800 feet high.

only a cornfield had been before; and Dionisio Polido will go down in history as the legal "owner" of a volcano, and as the discoverer of one of the greatest eruptions that has taken place in modern Mexico, and certainly the greatest natural spectacle ever seen by the inhabitants of that country for several generations.

From far away it had also been seen and heard. The earthquake tremors had been recorded on seismographs as far distant as New York and South America. People from all over the state rushed to see what had happened. But before the spectators arrived, the shooting fire and billowing steam and ashes had caused panic, not only in the near-by village of Parícutin, but also in San Juan Parangaricutiro and other villages. The mayor of San Juan called on the Governor of the State of Michoacan for help; the Governor wired to the President in Mexico City, and at once the Government set to work to help move the people away from danger.

The cattle in the valley ran about, bellowing with terror, while the once friendly cornfield belched fire, sand, and ashes high above them, only to fall again on their barns and pastures.

Parícutin grew with remarkable rapidity. When it was one week old, its cone was 550 feet high; within ten weeks, 1,100 feet. Up to this time it was a true cinder cone, that is, all of its material had come from fragments that had been blown into the air and had fallen back to build up the cone.

Two days after the first explosion, lava flowed from a fissure in a field about a thousand feet north of the explosion vent (but no lava came from the cone until nearly four months later when it broke through the side of the cone). In five days this first flow of lava was 2,000 feet long and 600 feet wide, and 20 feet thick at the sides and front. It grew for about six weeks until it was 6,000 feet long, 3,000 feet wide, and more than 100 feet high, slowly pushing over the countryside and destroying every living thing it touched, whether plant or animal.

4

Three Lions

TWO MONTHS OLD AND AT LEAST 800 FEET HIGH.
Rocks, still hot and steaming, are piled in great, glowing heaps
on all sides of the mountain. The trees are beginning to show the
weight of the ashes upon their branches.

5

By this time everyone realized that the entire valley was in danger of being devastated. How terrifying it must have been for the farmers and villagers in the valley to know that their homes were doomed to be buried by the approaching lava that spread out over the valley and flowed at the rate of several feet an hour! It was estimated that in the first few days of the lava flow, an area of more than a million square yards had been inundated by the lava.

This volcano is an awe-inspiring sight to thousands of people from all parts of the country; but it is of especial interest to scientists. Very seldom have geologists had an opportunity to watch a volcano develop from the day of its birth. So they were very prompt to install scientific instruments on the near-by mountaintops to measure the intensity of the eruptions; and geologists are ever at hand to measure the spread of lava flow. They have named the volcano "El Parícutin" from the village which was its first victim.

The visitors during the first few weeks estimated that there were thirty to forty eruptions a minute, all accompanied by deafening explosions. The column of steam and dust rose to a height of more than 4,500 feet, while rocks and fragments of lava that were thrown from the crater reached an altitude of 1,500 to 3,000 feet.

During the afternoon of June 9, violent explosions shook the earth, the dust quieted down, and large bombs of soft, melted rock were thrown out which hardened while sailing through the air. All night the earthquakes, the ear-shattering explosions, and the violent discharge of bombs continued.

Early in the morning of June 10, all activity stopped for a few uneasy minutes, and only a cloud of dust hung over the volcano and hid it from sight. Among the watchers that night and morning was Dr. Frederick H. Pough, curator of geology and minerology of the American Museum of Natural History, New York; and he reported that as soon as the volcano became visible, he

6

Three Lions

NOT ONLY SCIENTISTS AND TRAVELERS COME TO WATCH THE VOLCANO, BUT INDIANS, TOO, WALK FOR MANY MILES TO SEE THIS WONDER OF MICHOACAN.

It is interesting to listen to their conversation, especially when they discuss their religious beliefs in connection with the causes of this volcano.

7

saw at once that a landslide had taken place in the night, breaking down the part of the crater nearest him, and that his party was able to watch the rocks tumbling down, making the break in the crater even deeper. They saw the cloud of gray dust turning red at various areas, because the iron in the rocks was oxidizing to a red oxide form. As they watched, boulders from the crater cracked open and showed a glowing interior. These hot boulders continued to fall, rolling down the side of the mountain, and on top of a lava flow that had taken place several weeks before, but had not yet cooled. In fact, the temperature of the flow was found by a pyrometer to be 1,600 degrees Fahrenheit—and that was three months after its escape from the earth's interior!

In the *Natural History Magazine* for October, 1943, Dr. Pough writes: "The most spectacular event of the recent history of Parícutin was the birth of a new lava flow, the first liquid flow, which took place around 7:30 in the evening of June 10th. . . . The writer resolved that he would have to have a look at it. . . . There was no alternative but to struggle up the slope which felt cool to the touch and safe to climb. On reaching the top, a bed of hot coals, looking for all the world like a tremendous furnace bed 100 feet across, was seen about ten feet below the ridge. As the tripod was being set up for some pictures, the ridge was felt to move a bit, so little time was wasted after the pictures were obtained. Within a few minutes, the hot bed thrust upwards and forward, toppling the ridge over, and the first liquid flow came out, with solid rocks of various sizes riding along on its surface. The lava advanced very rapidly, for it was coming down a moderate slope and covered several hundred feet within an hour. . . . From subsequent reports, this flow seems to have continued until it reached the now abandoned village of Parícutin."

Thus the geologists watch the movements of its lava flows, and keep records of its activity and development.

8

Three Lions

BY THE TIME THIS TERRIBLE INFANT WAS FOUR MONTHS OLD, it had built a cone 1,000 feet high, about 1,000 feet across at the top, and about 3,000 feet across at its base. The picture shows a lava stream coming out of the middle of the slope.

9

So far, no people have been killed by this volcano; but homes, farms, and numberless trees have been destroyed by its ashes and lava. It has blighted the whole region. Not a tree, a bush, or a blade of grass is now alive within many miles of the volcano, in what had been a fertile valley. Lovely pine trees filled the forest, and the natives gathered turpentine from them. But now the trees stand black and lifeless. Far, far away, wherever the wind spreads a thick blanket of ashes, all vegetation withers and dies. Water is scarce, for the springs have gone dry, and birds drop dead from the skies. Since the volcano's beginning, cattle, even in faraway villages, have become thinner and thinner, from lack of green grass to eat.

The village of Parícutin is practically obliterated under its cover of sand, ash, volcanic debris, and lava. From time to time, new flows issue from vents around the mountain. When Parícutin was about eight months old, a new cone, which the natives called *Zapicho* (or Little Fellow), opened up on its side. It became violently active, sending out liquid lava, bombs, and fragmentary materials until it built up a semicircular cone 210 feet high on the side of Parícutin. Soon after this the main crater became less active, and finally became entirely quiet except for the escape of steam and gas.

In January, 1944, a group of daring young Mexican explorers descended into the main crater and remained for several seconds —long enough for one of their number to photograph the others within the smoky pit for a Mexican newspaper. Other climbers have ventured to the rim of the crater.

Zapicho, the parasite, died in January, 1944, and its orifice was sealed so that now one can walk upon it in perfect safety. Soon after Zapicho became silent, a new vent which was called *Taqui* opened on the other side of the mountain. Taqui has sent out one of the most spectacular flows yet seen at Parícutin. Its lava extended all the way around to the other side of the cone, and then reached out toward the village of San Juan Parangari-

10

cutiro, four miles away. In time it reached this village and destroyed it. A newspaper report from Uruapan, Mexico, of June 27, 1944, states: "Military trucks were in Parangarieutiro today to remove the last of the inhabitants as the lava from the Parícutin volcano broke through a wall of rock and advanced on the town again."

At the time of this writing, the volcano is still active, though less vehemently than formerly, and with periods of rest. If its activity continues, doubtless many scientists from overseas will visit it, now that the war is over; but up to the present time only those of the Americas have had easy access to it.

No one knows what the future of this volcano will be, what it will do, or how long it will last. Dr. Ralph R. Bodle, seismologist of the U.S. Coast and Geodetic Survey, who also was present when the liquid lava flow broke out on June 10, met a Mexican who was helping to evacuate the people of Parícutin, then partially covered by lava. The native said to him, very truthfully, "Many learned people come here to study the volcano; they write articles; but with all their knowledge, not one of them can tell you when the volcano is going to stop."

Dr. Pough says, "Perhaps Parícutin will continue for many years; perhaps it will die down shortly. When it is finished it will never erupt again, for the cinder cones which dot the countryside are clearly the products of a single, continuous eruption. So while it is active, it should be studied in the greatest detail, and it is well worth a visit, despite the many inconveniences, for any who can get there."

11

American Museum of Natural History

How Exciting Is the First View of the Volcano in the Distance!

As the traveler approaches the volcano, the very air bristles with excitement. Even while many miles away, the cloud of steam and dust may be seen in the distance, curling into fantastic shapes in the sky. The thunders of explosions are heard many miles distant, and may test the courage of the more timid traveler.

Visitors to Parícutin may go from Mexico City by train or by automobile; or they may soar over the volcano in a plane if they prefer to see it in that way. The nearest town where a comfortable hotel may be found is Uruapan, about twenty miles from the volcano. The trip from Uruapan may be made by car or by local bus, but it is necessary to travel the last few miles on horses, mules, or burros, because of the deep ash and uneven terrain.

All the way from Uruapan the ashes are evident on the road, and they become deeper and deeper until the driver has much difficulty in keeping the wheels from sinking. It rains every day

12

in the vicinity of the active volcano, and if the rain should happen to catch the traveler in thick, soft ashes, he may become hopelessly stuck in the mud and greatly delayed on his journey, as was the writer's party in the summer of 1943.

For miles between Uruapan and San Juan, as we rode along, short, brown cornstalks stood in rows like soldiers in uniform on fields of deep, dark ashes. Only a few months before, these stalks had been green, with young ears of corn, tassels, and long shiny leaves. But now their broken stubs stood as tombstones over the grave of the last crop of corn that will grow on these fields for many a year to come.

Soon there appeared in the distance not only the gray cloud of curling "smoke," but also the dark mound from which it was coming, with many curls of white steam boiling up all around the mound. We had to transfer to the horses before we could cross the gullies and the deep volcanic ash that lay everywhere, and climb the hill from which the spectacle could be watched. A few miles more and we were among the dead trees—pine trees black and needleless, gradually being buried. Another steep, black mound to climb, and we were directly in front of the mighty smoking mountain, with white steam on all sides of it, rising from the hot lava that had been thrown from the crater.

Three Lions

WE WERE STUNNED BY THE OVERPOWERING SPECTACLE BE-
FORE US, which the camera describes far better than words. In
the foreground is an ancient crater receiving gifts from another

14

generation of craters; and trees that are gray from the rain of ashes.

In order to obtain a nearer view, we were led by our Mexican guides down on the other side of the hill, and we climbed up to a spot where the Mexican Government had built a shelter giving an excellent view of the great spectacle. Under the shelter a Mexican woman was busy at a little charcoal stove preparing hot soup for the visitors, which was most gratefully accepted, for the air had grown very cold. But the heat from the volcano soon warmed all the shivering travelers.

There it was, before our very eyes, and apparently so near to us: an awesome, terrifying thing. The huge black pile of cinders, rocks, and lava, and the white steam rising from its base all around it; the boiling, gaseous, foamlike clouds coming out of the crater in thick, massive rolls, and being pushed upward, higher and higher, by more gases and more rolls from beneath. The gray and black masses of cloud rolled upward for thousands of feet. Then suddenly appeared huge rolls of red-brown that swerved outward and curled upward, pushing the gray rolls higher still, and they, in turn, were pushed by more clouds of gray and black and reddish brown—like monstrous infernal flowers unfolding—all rushing upward as if each dark, curling roll wanted to be the first to get its message to heaven.

At intervals the graceful curves of the rolling dust clouds were broken by explosions that sent bombs and cinders shooting through them. The roaring cannonade was deafening to our ears, and gave proof that some terrific force was at work inside this huge cauldron; and it seemed no wonder that everything wanted to escape and be free. With explosion after explosion, great masses of red-hot rock shot high into the air, fell back, and went rolling down the volcano's steep, dark sides.

15

Three Lions

LIKE A HEAVY CURTAIN, DARKNESS DROPPED QUICKLY. AND NOW THE FLYING BOMBS AND CINDERS GLOWED ORANGE AND RED, CLEARLY AGAINST THE BLACKNESS OF THE NIGHT.

This extraordinary night photograph shows a stream of lava pushing its way out and down the side of the ever erupting vol-

16

cano. The travelers and trees in the foreground, silhouetted by vapor from the lava between them and the volcano, are dwarfed by the 1,500-foot mountain.

The gray and brown clouds that had been boiling up all afternoon doubtless continued after darkness fell, but they were no longer visible; and the fiery red rocks and cinders now had an opportunity to stage a brilliant pyrotechnical display. Huge chunks of red-hot lava shot up, whirled around, and gracefully turned to answer the pull of gravity. Some of them fell back into the seething cauldron, and others rolled, still red-hot, down the sides and out of sight. Blacker the smoke and redder the fire, as darker grew the night. A booming explosion, and tons of red-hot rocks burst above the crater and hurled themselves down to pile up ever higher and higher, in this wild and furious building of another mountain on the face of Mexico.

A moment's pause—a great shudder—another deafening, thunderous explosion, and now the orange-hot and red-hot liquid lava comes rolling and tumbling in mad fury over the edge of the crater. It runs in wide, glistening streams down the mountainsides like waterfalls of fire, and on to its destiny of ruin and destruction to farmlands and villages miles beyond.

We are all silenced with awe by these stupendous forces of nature. We cannot speak, even if we would. We can only look, and let this blazing, gigantic moving picture burn itself into our memories. Neither can we think. It is too much for human beings to understand; we can only leave our minds a blank and let what will, come in. The experience of having really seen this great spectacle in all its terrifying grandeur is enough.

17

Three Lions

THE MOUNTAIN CONTINUES TO GROW.

This photograph was taken in October, 1943, three months later than the view on page 14. Notice the height of the lava formation at the right, as compared with the earlier picture. This great heap was pushed up 250 feet by an underground lava stream beneath it. The steam and gases find their way from the hot lava through the thick layers of ashes above it.

18

After seeing a volcano in action, or reading about it, various questions naturally arise in one's mind: What is the cause of these explosions within the earth? Where does this terrific force come from, and where is it likely to break out? Are some of our own fields and valleys in danger? Do they ever appear in the sea, as well as on land? Where are the other volcanoes of the world? Do they all behave as Parícutin behaves?

Although Parícutin, so far, has not destroyed human lives, this is because people have kept out of its way, and the villagers had sufficient warning to flee, and leave their homes and their fields to be destroyed by the monster. It is easy to see that nothing in man's power (at present) can control the deadly onslaught of these destructive forces. What has happened when people do not have warning? How has mankind in other places suffered from volcanoes? The region around Parícutin was only thinly settled; what happens when a volcano breaks out in a thickly settled region?

Some of these questions must still remain in the realm of wondering, for scientists do not yet agree on the answers. In the National Research Council's latest report on volcanoes, Dr. Immanuel Friedlaender writes: "The science of volcanology is still in its infancy, and is not founded on exact knowledge and understanding of the phenomena. . . . As for the main question—what a volcano really is, how it works, how different volcanoes are connected with each other and with the interior of the earth, or whether they are connected at all with it—there does not exist any agreement of opinions."

Therefore the following pages will be devoted to showing some of the directions in which volcanologists are thinking, rather than attempting to give definite answers concerning the causes of volcanic action. Other questions concerning where other volcanoes are located, how they behave, and how mankind has suffered from them will be more clearly answered in later chapters.

19

2:

The Causes of Volcanic Activity

As is well known, a volcano is an opening in the earth through which hot materials come forth from deep below the surface. These materials, coming through a vent, or crater, at the top, often build up a shape like a mountain; but this is not always the case. Sometimes a volcano has only one large vent at the summit; often there are other openings in the sides of the mound. Volcanic eruptions may also take place through a long crack, or fissure, where steam and other heated materials escape, or through a row of openings following the crack. In size, volcanoes, as we see them on earth today, range from small cones no larger than a haystack to the highest mountains on the globe.

Hundreds of great mountains that now stand on the face of the earth were built from hot materials thrown out from the interior millions of years ago, and others have been built within historical times. In the early periods of the earth's history, before human beings existed, volcanoes must have been plentiful and exceedingly violent, judging from the volcanic mountains and great fields of lava spread over so many parts of the earth. All through the ages they must have played an important part in shaping the surface of the earth, though they probably have not made as many changes as water has made. The work of volcanoes is still going on, for there are hundreds of them now active in the world.

What is this great force, and what makes it necessary for it to break through everything in its path and send out to the surface these parts of the earth's interior? This is a question that has puzzled the minds of men ever since men have had minds that

20

were capable of wondering. It would be interesting to know what primitive man thought of the terrifying behavior of volcanoes, but no doubt he fitted them into his ideas of religion, and made whatever gods he worshiped responsible for them. "Fire-breathing mountains" are mentioned in the Bible, but no explanation of them is given there.

The ancient Greeks and Romans thought a smoking mountain was the chimney of Vulcan's forge. Vulcan was the god of fire and metals (or the blacksmith god), and it was from this Latin name (Vulcanus or Volcanus) that the word "volcano" was derived. On a small island in the Mediterranean Sea is a "fire-breathing mountain" which was thought by the ancients to be the very workshop of Vulcan where he forged the thunderbolts of the gods. Very often they heard, from below, sounds as of a mighty hammer on a vast anvil, and through this mountain's vent came the black smoke and red glow of what they considered the fires of Vulcan's forge. They gave the mountain the name of Vulcano. Vulcano is still an active volcano; and although it is scarcely known today, its name clings to all the fire-breathing mountains of the earth.

In olden times volcanoes were regarded with superstitious awe, and, for many people, it would have been considered wicked to make any investigations of their actions. We are told by Virgil that Mt. Etna marks the spot where the gods in their anger buried Enceladus, one of the rebellious giants. The later Greeks were the first to attempt a scientific explanation of volcanoes. Plato considered the source of lava streams to be a subterranean river of fire, and thought the eruptions were caused by the force of air that was under great pressure. Aristotle, also, refers to the force of "pent-up winds," and several of the later Roman writers tried to explain the cause of Mt. Etna's behavior.

This globe upon which we live has always been an interesting subject of study, and in more recent times the development of the science of geology has added much to our knowledge, not

21

only of the visible surface of the earth, but also of that part which lies beneath. Geologists have given us much information that throws light on the causes of volcanoes; and that special branch of geology called volcanology (or vulcanology) has become an important field of study. Volcanologists have advanced several different theories of the cause of volcanoes, but, so far, no one really knows just what happens inside the earth to bring a volcano into being.

In order to understand as much as we can of these interesting phenomena, it would be well to think for a moment of the earth as a whole. It is about 4,000 miles from the surface to the center of the earth. Geologists speak of the 40 or 50 miles nearest the surface as "the crust of the earth"—which is very thin compared to the remaining 3,960 miles, more or less, from the "crust" to the center of the earth.

Man has not been able to probe very deeply into the crust. Of the deepest wells that have been drilled, the deepest mines that have been excavated, and the deepest tunnels that have been cut, none has reached a depth of more than a very few miles below the surface. But even these have brought some knowledge of the earth's interior. Studies of the temperature in deep wells, mines, and tunnels show that the heat increases as the depth increases— usually about one degree for every 60 or 70 feet, though the rate is different in different places; and it has been estimated that the inside of the crust, at a depth of twenty or thirty miles, may possibly be at 4,000 degrees centigrade. It is difficult to imagine how hot that is, since only 100 degrees is boiling! From this fact, and from the evidence of what volcanoes send forth, most scientists of today agree that the entire interior of the earth is exceedingly hot.

Until after the invention of the seismograph (an instrument which records the tremors of the earth in earthquakes) it was believed that the interior of the earth was liquid—a mass of molten rock—that may have dated back to the early days of the

22

earth's existence as a planet. But the sensitive needle of the seismograph, recording earthquake tremors, has shown that some of the waves travel directly through the center of the earth in the same manner in which they travel through a steel ball, and not as they would travel through a liquid mass. In view of this fact, we can no longer believe that the inside of the earth is a liquid.

Scientists now explain that although it is hot enough to be a liquid (so far as its *temperature* is concerned), the enormous pressure upon this internal mass keeps it rigid, and will not allow it to take on a liquid form. In order to melt, rock must expand; and if the great pressure around it will not allow enough room for that expansion, it cannot melt, and remains solid, no matter how hot it may be. It is well known that substances change their states and appear as solids, liquids, or gases, depending on the temperature and pressure. It is easy to believe that the pressure in the earth's interior is enormous—the deeper, the more pressure—since at every level the rock must carry the weight of everything above it. It has been estimated that at a depth of ten miles, the pressure upon every square inch of rock is at least thirty-five tons.

The pressure and the heat are accepted as facts by the geologists; but they are still uncertain as to the *cause of the heat.* Some think that it is caused by the great internal pressure; for it can be proved in any laboratory that pressure does produce heat. In more recent years, the discovery of radioactivity has shown that heat is produced when the chemical elements of the earth disintegrate and break down into other substances (uranium into plutonium, etc.), and it has been claimed that radioactive changes that are taking place within the earth produce enough heat for volcanic action. Future discoveries in the field of science will probably bring new theories of the origin of the earth's internal heat, and it is quite possible that several of the supposed causes, combined, may be at work.

Another geological fact seems to play a very important part

in causing volcanoes. We know that the surface of the earth is continually changing, and geologists have pointed out that these changes are taking place not only because of what happens on the surface from water and weather, but also because of what is happening in the crust of the earth below the surface. For a long time it was thought that the earth is gradually cooling and its crust wrinkling, just as the skin of a baked apple wrinkles when it cools; and that this wrinkling of the earth's outer layers makes folds in the rocky crust that produce mountains, plateaus, valleys, and ocean basins. But in recent years this "cooling" theory has been questioned.

We know that earthquakes are caused by movements within the earth's crust. The earth is never free from earthquakes. It has been estimated that an earthquake severe enough to be felt at some place in the world occurs about every minute or two; therefore we know that there must be movements in the earth's crust taking place continually. Great blocks of the earth's crust move, sea bottoms sink or slowly heave upward into ranges of mountains, and even whole continents move up or down or sidewise. We know that the rocks of the earth's crust have been folding, breaking, and slipping for ages; and we also know, from sea shells found embedded in mountain rocks, that seas and mountains were not always where we now find them.

Some geologists think that the movements are caused by the difference in weight of the rocks of the earth's crust, the heavier blocks sinking toward the center of the earth, leaving the lighter ones to be squeezed upward. The great hollows in which the oceans lie are thus believed to be underlaid by heavier and more solid rocks, while the land masses are built of the lighter rocks, and so stand at a higher level. Because of this weight, or downward pressure, great blocks in the crust of the earth move downward in places where the deep rocks are weak, or where some of the underlying rocks have been removed in the form of lava. When such a movement occurs, the sunken rocks may form a deep basin, or they may break, and one side slip past the other. These movements that take place by breaking are called "faultings"; the crack or fissure is called "a fault," and the ridges formed on the surface as a result of this slipping are called "fault cliffs" or "scarps." Sometimes great plateaus are uplifted, and valleys, too, may be formed in this way. The great Rift Valley of Africa was formed by a large block of the crust of the earth dropping down several thousand feet, leaving vertical walls on the sides.

What generates the enormous forces that bend and break the rocks? the force that drops a valley and pushes up the sea floor until it becomes a lofty highland? We still do not know. The *cause* of these fractures and shiftings of the rocks within the earth is another one of the great mysteries of science.

But whatever the causes, scientists agree that this shifting of the position of the interior rocks changes the pressure and leaves some places where the strain of the burden they carry is less than at other places, making "weak spots" in the earth's crust. When a layer of rock breaks, and one piece slips down, or is pushed up from its former position, the deep crack or fault becomes a weak line. Since the blocks of broken rock are sometimes enormous, a fault may be hundreds of miles long. Very often two cracks cross each other, making a downward "tunnel" that is doubly weak. Scientists also agree that it is along the routes of these weak places in the earth's crust that the volcanic material finds its most favorable channel for exit to the surface.

The question as to what "sets off" the volcanic action is still a matter for discussion. The theory most generally accepted at present is that pressure, in combination with a newly made fault, or with some form of internal shifting, starts the volcanic action. As already stated, the rock of the earth's interior is hot enough to be in liquid form were it not for the enormous pressure upon it; but this pressure keeps it solid and rigid until at some point the pressure is sufficiently reduced (by breaking or slipping of

25

the rocks above it) for some of this rigid, hot rock to take on its liquid form (lava). As a liquid, it can now be squeezed up into the crevices above it by the greater pressure below it. Molten lava, especially when under great pressure, has the capacity to dissolve great volumes of gas; and it is known that lava contains great amounts of various kinds of combustible gases while still in the earth's interior. As the lava ascends through the weak spots, the pressure upon these gases becomes less and less, and they form bubbles which make the lava still lighter, and the rate of ascent becomes more rapid. Finally, the gases within the liquid become free to explode (as a bottle of soda water "explodes" when the pressure of the bottle cap is removed), and they blow out a passageway along the path of the weakest spots, always pushing through where there is less and less pressure, until the lava reaches the surface. A long fissure with other cracks breaking into it may provide several weak places, thus forming a long series of volcanoes—a remarkable instance of this being the island of Java.

Another theory is that the cracks between the rocks allow water from the various underground basins, or even from the earth's surface, to flow or seep down until it reaches the very hot rocks below. When the water reaches these overheated strata, it explodes into volumes of steam (in the same way that steam rises when a little water is spilled on a hot stove), and if there is no free vent to the surface, the steam blows its way out, tearing the earth open, and bringing with it whatever lies in the way. Superheated steam is one of the most powerful of all explosives.

Others have suggested that after the internal pressure has started the upward journey of the liquid lava, it may meet a stream of water which would set off the steam explosions and help to blow the channel open.

Once a volcanic channel or "chimney" has been opened by explosion, it is probable that gas pressure alone may bring about other eruptions. Even in a volcano that has been quiet for a hun-

26

dred years or more, its chimney may be plugged with hardened lava that was left behind in its last explosion; hot gases may rise and start to melt the plug; hot fluid lava may rise again and add its pressure to the gases that are melting the plug, until finally the plug is blown out in bits with a great gas explosion, and the fresh lava has a free passageway to flow out.

All of the above theories that relate to the causes of volcanism have some facts to support them; and as more and more facts are gleaned from new discoveries in the field of science, some of the present mysteries will doubtless be cleared away. In the meantime, we have a body of organized knowledge based on studies of volcanoes themselves, their different forms of action, their distribution, appearance, the materials they eject, etc.; and these phases of volcanology will be briefly touched upon in the next three chapters.

3:

Volcanic Materials

Magma—The molten rock material within the earth, plus whatever gases it may contain, is called "magma," which means "dough." After it rises to the surface, it is usually spoken of as "lava." This molten material rising from the depths is always more or less highly charged with gases; but as the magma rises in a volcanic vent, these gases begin to escape because of the decreasing pressure on the liquid as it nears the earth's surface; and after it is ejected, by the time the liquid solidifies, the gases are almost wholly eliminated. Magmas differ greatly in composition; for example, the lava erupted by Vesuvius is very unlike that which is discharged by Etna. Furthermore, many a long-lived volcano has erupted lava of different kinds. No one knows the reason for these differences; but it is thought that the "parent magma" the world over is basaltic* in composition. One of the reasons for this belief is that the great fissure eruptions (or flows of lava from fissures in the earth's crust) that have taken place in past ages and have discharged such enormous volumes of lava are, with few exceptions, of basaltic composition. The great lava fields of the Columbia Plateau and the Deccan Traps (see p. 41) are of basalt. This seems to show that basalt in a form that will become liquid when pressure is relieved underlies the visible crust; and that at any place where the pressure is sufficiently reduced, the basalt melts and a body of magma forms which again becomes hard basalt after it flows upon the surface and hardens.

The chief gas in magma is steam, or water vapor. The combustible gases—hydrogen, sulphur, hydrocarbons—are also in

---

* Basalt is a dark, hard rock—the commonest kind of hardened lava. Basalt may be black, brown, dark green, or dark gray.

28

the magma. Their combustion, especially that of hydrogen, produces the only true flames seen at a volcanic eruption.

The rise of magma to the earth's surface has been compared to the action of a press. The earth's crust has been broken into great blocks, or segments, and these have, at times, moved up or down with respect to one another. In some regions where great blocks of this kind, measuring hundreds of thousands of square miles, have sunk, this sinking has brought about the rise of magma and outpouring of lava. Such sinking of the crust and accompanying volcanic activity have occurred in the great Rift Valley of eastern Africa and the valley of the Rhine.

As a rule, volcanoes eject gases, liquids, and solids. The gases usually appear first and continue all through an eruption. They blow out the solid materials that are blocking the passageway, and the liquids, coming from deeper down, follow later.

Gases—The enormous clouds that rise to such great height in many eruptions show that the amount of steam discharged by an active volcano is immense. It is the main explosive agent in all volcanic eruptions. When steam is heated to 800 or 900 degrees centigrade, it exerts an explosive pressure upon whatever surrounds it, greater than that of any common artificial explosive. Less violent explosions merely throw materials out, but those explosions that are very violent shatter material into dust. This dust is of extremely irregular and jagged shapes which are characteristic of volcanic dust. The so-called smoke which is seen to come out of volcanoes is chiefly steam that is made black at the time of explosion by the enormous quantity of very fine dust suspended with the steam.

The steam given out from the crater soon condenses to rain, which mixes with the ashes and loose material that has been ejected and forms mud which may rush down the cone and spread far and wide. A torrent of mud is sometimes one of the first symptoms of a violent eruption. The city of Herculaneum was buried beneath a flood of mud which swept down from Vesuvius during

29

the eruption of 79 A.D. The eruptions and rains are often accompanied by lightning and other electrical displays caused, perhaps, by the friction of the particles in the air, and by atmospheric disturbances.

During an actual volcanic eruption, the gases probably include gaseous water, or steam, though this varies with different volcanoes and at different stages of an eruption. Besides the steam, many other gases are exhaled by volcanoes. They come not only from the crater or other opening, but also from cracks and fumeroles on the sides of volcanoes, and from the flows of lava which continue for weeks to throw off gases as they cool and harden. Carbon dioxide, hydrochloric acid, hydrofluoric acid, and hydrogen are given off. Various compounds of sulphur, such as hydrogen sulphide and sulphur dioxide, are emitted by some but not all volcanoes. The important part that gases play in bringing volcanic materials to the surface has already been explained.

Solid Materials—The rocky materials blown into the air by the explosions of the gases are called the "fragmental products." They are derived from the crust of hardened lava that was left in the upper part of the "chimney" after a previous eruption; or from rock material torn from the walls of the deep passageway; or from lava pushed out from the top of the liquid column by the gases that are violently escaping from the magma. Although these clots of lava, torn from the top of the rising column, start their flight in the liquid state, they usually harden in the air and fall as solid fragments. The rock and the clots of molten lava that are blown out and solidified vary greatly in size—from dust so fine that it floats in the atmosphere for several years, to large masses weighing many tons. They are roughly classified according to size, as follows: Pieces the size of an apple or larger are called *blocks* if they are ejected as solid pieces, and *bombs* if ejected as clots of still fluid magma; those the size of a nut are called *lapilli* (Latin for "little stones"); those the size of a pea are *volcanic ashes,* and the finest are *volcanic dust.*

30

VOLCANIC ASHES HAVE ALMOST COMPLETELY BURIED
THIS SCHOOLHOUSE IN JAPAN.

If the lava is granulated, it is called *volcanic sand*. Ashes and lapilli are often spoken of as *volcanic cinders*, or *scoriea*. The coarser material falls around the vent; the finer material, carried by the wind, tends to fall after the coarser has fallen, and at greater distances from the vent. The coarser material, when converted into rock, is termed *volcanic breccia;* and the finer material—the dust and ashes—is known as *tuff*. Rock which consists

31

of several kinds of ejected materials, including large blocks, is called *volcanic agglomerate*. Volcanic cinders, sand, ashes, dust, etc., are all varied forms of solidified lava.

Liquid Material—This is the lava or molten rock that is pushed out to the surface. When lava first flows out, it is either white-hot or red-hot, but as it loses some of its terrific heat, it turns gray and gradually darker. Even while lava is in its most liquid form, it is not as thin as water. It is more or less sticky, or "viscous," like melted tar or liquid glue. As it cools it thickens and becomes more like dough, growing gradually thicker and stiffer until it forms a crust over the top, and later the entire lava flow becomes hard.

Very fluid lava moves rapidly, especially on steep slopes. Its rate of flow depends not only on the slope down which it runs, but also on how viscous or sticky it is, and how long it takes to harden. Some flows have averaged ten miles an hour, but five miles an hour is more usual. The lava from Parícutin was flowing at the rate of about seven miles an hour. At Vesuvius in 1805, a velocity of fifty miles an hour at the moment of emission was recorded; and in 1929, the lava from Mt. Etna was said to descend from the crater at a speed of twenty feet a minute, or less than a quarter of a mile per hour. Sometimes a very thick mass of lava creeps slowly forward for months, or even years, before it becomes hard enough to stop completely. Sometimes a crust forms over the top while the under part is still moving, and this crust may break up into rough, jagged blocks and be carried along by the slow-moving lava. When the flow finally hardens and comes to rest, these broken pieces make the lava sheet extremely rough on the surface and difficult to walk or drive over. In the Southwest, such *block lava* is called "malpais," a Spanish word meaning "bad country." The geologic name is *aa* lava.

After a stream of lava has become crusted over and hard on the surface, if the underlying magma should flow away, a long cavern or tunnel may be formed. The walls and roof of a lava cave are occasionally adorned with stalactites, while the floor may be covered with stalagmite deposits of lava. There are beautiful examples of such lava caves in Hawaii and also at the Craters of the Moon, in Idaho.

Not all lavas harden in the same way. Sometimes a hardened lava field has a very smooth surface. Other lavas harden with smooth surfaces which have curious ropy, billowy forms, like the icing that has run over the top of a cake, as shown in the illustration below. This is known as *ropy* or *corded lava*. *Pahoehoe*, a Hawaiian word, is the accepted term for this.

U.S. Geological Survey

LAVA CASCADE, HAWAII. THE BASALT HAS SOLIDIFIED AS CORDED LAVA, OR PAHOEHOE.

In some cases the lava solidifies in such a way as to make buns or pillow-shaped masses within the lava, forming *pillow lava,* but in other cases, no such internal structure develops. There are fine ancient examples of pillow lava in Glacier National Park,

33

from fissure flows on the bottom of an ancient sea. Lava which is exposed to the air cools rapidly, and in cooling it shrinks, and in shrinking it cracks, sometimes forming the kind of thing which has been made so famous by the Giant's Causeway in Ireland. Here the surface cracked in six-sided blocks, and as the cracks went deeper and deeper, straight down into the lava flow, the rock finally broke into pillars or columns. This kind of break is often referred to as *columnar jointing*. (See illustration below.) Columnar jointing is common in flows of New Jersey, Idaho, and the Columbia Plateau. An especially fine example is the Devil's Tower in Wyoming.

U.S. Geological Survey

COLUMNAR STRUCTURE. PALISADES OF THE
COLUMBIA RIVER, WASHINGTON.

34

Hardened lavas are of different colors, depending on the chemical composition of the magma that produced the rock. It may be a black basalt or a light-colored lava called "rhyolite," or it may be of intermediate character called "andesite." Black basalt is the material of most of the great fissure eruptions, such as the Columbia Plateau and the Deccan Traps; but the light-colored rhyolites have been poured out in some regions on a similar grand scale. The Rhyolite Plateau of Yellowstone National Park seems to have been formed in this way by fissure eruptions.

Igneous rocks—The parent magma from deep in the earth is the source of all the igneous, or once hot rocks. ("Igneous" comes from the Latin word for fire.) As their name shows, igneous rocks were formed at high temperatures. Some are exceedingly strong and durable; some also have great beauty and richness, and those that combine both qualities will always be in demand for buildings or other monuments designed for permanence. Igneous rocks are classified according to their texture: coarse-grained, fine-grained, and glassy. The more slowly the magma cools, the coarser is the grain size. When it cools very rapidly, the gases escape quickly without having time to form bubbles, and it produces a glass. Grain size also depends upon the order of formation and minerals present. Some glass is very bubbly. The controlling factor in the formation of a nonbubbly glass is very high viscosity.

Magma is made up of two parts. A volatile (easily evaporated or vaporized) part amounts to a few per cent. This consists of gaseous water with carbon dioxide, sulphur fumes, and other fumes. The other part of the magma is nonvolatile, and consists chiefly of molten minerals called "silicates." The volatile part makes the magma more fluid; but by the time it becomes solid, practically all the volatile part has escaped, and it is the molten silicas that crystallize and form the rocks.

There are three principal kinds of magmas according to the amount of silicas they contain, and these are called *silicic, inter-*

35

mediate, and *basic.* Silicic magma, when it hardens, forms granite and rhyolite; intermediate magma forms diorite and andesite; and basic magma forms gabbro and basalt—all of these according to the conditions under which the magma solidifies.

As magmas differ in chemical composition, so will the igneous rocks differ, and will have different amounts of silica, oxides of metal, etc., in them. The names used by scientists for a few important kinds of igneous rock are: granite, diorite, gabbro, pyroxenite, hornblendite, rhyolite, rhyolite porphyry, andesite, basalt, dolerite.

Volcanic glasses occur as lava flows which have cooled rapidly, or as thin crusts on the surface of other flows. Lustrous volcanic glass is called *obsidian;* the duller variety is *pitchstone.* Obsidian is generally dark-colored to black.

U.S. Geological Survey

YELLOW PUMICE ADHERING TO A BASALT CINDER.

Pumice is frothed glass, and is usually white or light-colored. (See the illustration.) Pumice is really nothing but lava blown full of holes and thrown out in a liquid condition into the air, where it cools. Very often it is so filled with bubbles that it floats, and sometimes it covers the surface of the sea for miles. Crushed pumice has been used as a scrubbing powder for centuries.

36

The Roots of Volcanoes—It is believed that ever since the beginning of geologic times, magma has been rising from the depths to the upward levels of the earth's crust. If it reached the surface it was either ejected through volcanoes, or was poured out in colossal amounts during fissure eruptions. But much of the rising magma did not reach the surface, but stopped within the rocky crust, where it solidified. Such bodies of solidified magma that have never reached the surface are called *intrusive bodies.* These bodies of intrusive, igneous rock range in size all the way from very small to enormous. They are the laccoliths, stocks, batholiths, dikes, and sills.

When the rising magma fills a steeply inclined or vertical crack, or a fissure that cuts the layers of rock at right angles, and hardens there, it is called a *dike.* (See the picture of dikes on p. 38). As lava rarely flows over the lip of the crater, but escapes through fissures in the sides of the volcano (especially in high volcanoes), these fissures also become filled with lava which hardens into rock, forming dikes. These dikes extend outward and downward from the vent as a center, and they serve as ribs to strengthen the volcanic cone.

Every extinct volcanic conduit, or chimney, if it could be traced downward, would be found to join an intrusive mass below. Or, if the conduit is feeding an active volcano, it would be found to extend into a body of magma—the volcanic reservoir.

When the rising magma flows between layers of rock, pushing up the layers above it, and hardening between the layers and parallel with them, it is called a *sill.* Dikes and sills may be a few yards or many miles long; they may be a fraction of an inch to thousands of feet thick. Some dikes reach the earth's surface, and others are never found unless they are exposed to view (as sills are also exposed) by long wearing away of the rocks and other materials that surround them.

DIKES CUTTING HORIZONTAL BEDS AT RIGHT ANGLES.
ALAMILLO CREEK, NEW MEXICO.

38

Exposed rocks are subject to all the effects of the weather. "Weathering" will crack and loosen and soften rock material and make it more easily washed away by streams or blown away by storms. The destructive or "wearing away" work of weather, wind, and water is called *erosion*. Erosion has uncovered dikes and sills in various parts of the earth. The best-known sill in America is the Palisades of the Hudson River.

If the rising magma, after pushing between layers in the form of a sill, arches up the overlying layers instead of continuing to spread out between the layers, a lens of liquid rock will be produced, resting on a floor of hard rock; and when this becomes solid, it forms a *laccolith* (meaning a lake of stone), or a kind of mound under the surface of the earth. Many laccoliths have been uncovered by erosion, some very large ones in Utah.

A *batholith* (stone of great depth) is another form of hardened magma that has been pushed up into the earth's crust, but it does not rest on a known floor or layer of rock, as does a laccolith. It goes down and down, to unknown depths in the earth's crust, larger and larger in size as the depth increases. Batholiths are enormous magmas of ages ago that never reached the surface except in some places where erosion of the rocks above them has brought some of these batholiths to view. The largest exposed batholith in the United States is in central Idaho, where 16,000 square miles of it has been uncovered. A much larger one of 110,000 square miles lies in the Coast Ranges of British Columbia. Batholiths form the cores of many mountains where, through the ages, the magma has become hardened into granite.

There is a direct connection between volcanism and the beginnings of ore deposits. Metalic minerals are found concentrated in the igneous rocks themselves, distributed through the igneous rock and through the adjoining rock. Thus volcanism not only transfers materials from the deep interior and spreads them over the surface of the earth, but it also concentrates mineral deposits to such a degree that they may become of value to mankind.

39

4:

Varieties of Volcanoes and Craters

Some volcanoes have a period of violent eruptions and later become quiet for perhaps fifty or a hundred years, then erupt again. Some, after piling up enormous mountains of materials they have thrown out, stop their work and remain quiet for thousands of years and give no further evidence of erupting again. Such are called *extinct* (finished or dead) volcanoes. Some of the high mountains in the western part of the United States, such as Mt. Rainier and Mt. Hood, are considered to be extinct volcanoes.

Those that are quiet at present, but have not been dead long enough for us to know whether or when they may break out again, are called *dormant* (sleeping) volcanoes. Popocatapetl, in Mexico, is probably dormant, though many consider it extinct. Various of the so-called extinct volcanoes may be only sleeping, and time alone can tell whether they are or not.

Those that are either erupting or show signs of disturbance, such as frequent tremors of the earth near them, rumbling noises, or escaping steam, are called *active* volcanoes. Parícutin and Vesuvius are active volcanoes.

Often nothing but steam appears over the opening, perhaps for many years, and such volcanoes seem to act as mere safety valves for the escape of internal steam. As they are more or less "gentle," people become so accustomed to them that they build homes, farms, and even villages on the sloping sides of such volcanoes. As we shall see in later chapters, they sometimes meet disaster.

When a new volcano breaks out on the globe, it may appear on dry land or in the sea; for it is the condition deep down in the earth, and the easiest pathway to the surface, that are the decid-

40

ing factors, with no regard to what may be on the outside. As we have seen, Parícutin started in a Mexican farmer's cornfield; another volcano of Mexico, Jorullo, sprang up in somewhat the same manner in 1759, in an indigo plantation. Great numbers of them break out at the bottom of the ocean and cause great disturbance of the waters. These are called *submarine* volcanoes. In some parts of the ocean, even at great depths, submarine volcanoes have piled up enough rocks, lava, and other materials to build islands of considerable size. They are called *volcanic islands*.

Volcanoes are not only grouped into active, dormant, and extinct. They are also thought of as belonging to different types according to the way they erupt.

Some volcanoes have no explosions. The lava seems to have found a crack, or a weak channel, extending all the way down to the molten basalt beneath the earth's crust, and the pressure from below simply pushes the lava up through these fissures, and out over the edge of whatever opening has been made. Great floods of lava have been discharged from deep, long cracks or fissures in the earth's crust, with no apparent connection with anything shaped like a mountain. These are called *fissure eruptions*. Since such enormous quantities of lava well forth, they are also called *mass eruptions*. Some of the greatest volcanic eruptions that have ever taken place in the world come from such fissures or cracks, without leaving a dome or cone of any kind. In the geologic past, fissure or mass eruptions have occurred many times on a huge scale. In fact, large parts of Washington, Oregon, Idaho, and northern California are covered with vast fields of lava poured out in prehistoric times. These huge lava flows have a nearly flat surface, and are called the "Basaltic Plains"—also called the "Columbia Plateau." (Refer to p. 204.) There are vast lava fields in the Deccan region of western India called the "Deccan Traps" or "Basalts" which cover at least 200,000 square miles, and in some

41

places reach a depth of over 6,000 feet.

We usually think of a volcano as a cone-shaped mountain with a crater, or open funnel, in the top of the cone, through which the various volcanic materials are thrown out. It is true that eruptions from such volcanoes can be magnificent and spectacular, as Parícutin has demonstrated, but they are only a small showing at the earth's surface of far mightier activities of the molten rock within the earth's crust. It is the vast outpourings of *fissure* volcanoes that have built great basaltic plateaus, and have transferred from beneath the surface to the open air many thousands of cubic miles of liquid rock, which show the grandest effects of volcanism. The greatest of fissure volcanoes seem to belong to ancient history.

There are volcanoes now active which, by their manner of erupting, seem closely related to the fissure volcanoes. They are the *quiet* volcanoes, from which the liquid lava merely flows out over the rim of the opening without exciting noises. Kilauea, on the island of Hawaii, is a fine example of the quiet type of volcano which is still active. In fact, the Hawaiian Islands themselves were built up with lava that was poured out upon the floor of the sea. There are also examples of the quiet, flowing type of volcano in Iceland.

Perhaps the best-known volcanoes belong to the type of *explosive* volcanoes which hurl cinders, dust, and hot rocks, with thunderous explosions, high into the air. Parícutin belongs to this type. Very often volcanoes vary their mode of activity with quiet lava flows between periods of explosive violence.

Volcanoes are also classified according to their shapes. The shape of a volcanic cone depends on the nature and material of its eruptions. If the cone is built up of cinders, volcanic ash, blocks, and other fragmental products, it is called a *cinder cone*. A cinder cone is usually high and steep compared to the area it covers, because the absence of lava allows the cinders to pile up

42

into a steep cone before the accumulating mass begins to slide. Cinder cones are the results of explosive eruptions, and are relatively small. The following photograph shows a cinder cone with pahoehoe lava in the foreground.

Hawaii National Park

A CINDER CONE IN THE KAMAKAIA HILLS, HAWAII.

When lava breaks through the sides of a volcano below the crater and fragmentary materials are ejected through this opening, a cone is formed on the side of the main volcano. Cones of this kind are called "parasitic" cones, or "lateral" cones. In the case of Parícutin, a parasitic cone was called The Little Fellow. At Mt. Etna, which rises to more than 10,800 feet, the eruptions usually come from lateral or side cracks, sometimes at least half-way down the mountain side. The flanks of Mt. Etna have become

43

dotted over with cones of this kind, and some of them rise to considerable height.

Those volcanoes that have been built mainly or entirely by the piling up of lava flows around a central vent usually cover a great area in proportion to their height. There are no sharp points at the summit, and on top they resemble an inverted plate or a shield; hence they are called *shield* volcanoes. They have been built up by flows of highly fluid lavas which spread wide, making thin, nearly horizontal sheets. The volcanoes of the Hawaiian Islands are of this type. Mauna Loa, a great sloping dome 13,675 feet above the water, is a magnificent example of a shield volcano.

In shield volcanoes the vent appears to be at a fairly high spot, and the lava builds up near this opening a kind of "lava dome" curving convexly down on all sides from the opening.

The great majority of volcanoes, including most of the largest volcanoes in the world, have a shape that is intermediate in form between the cinder cone and the shield volcano. They are built up by two kinds of volcanic activity: by the fall of fragmental products around the opening when there are violent explosions, and by the discharge of lava flows when they erupt quietly. The deposits made by the different eruptions are marked by layers, some of coarser and some of finer material, which form a kind of bedding which slopes down and outward from the crater. These coarser and finer materials gradually become packed and cemented together. At times liquid lava flows down the outer slopes of the growing cone, and when these streams of lava solidify, they protect the more crumbly layers of breccia and tuff under them from erosion, and give strength to the volcanic pile. On account of the well-marked layers, or strata, produced by the alternation of tuff and breccia beds with sheets of lava, a cone of this kind is called a *strato*-volcano.

CRATER OF SAN MIGUEL VOLCANO, SAN SALVADOR, CENTRAL AMERICA.

This picture shows an air view of the quietly steaming crater inside the rim of an older crater of San Miguel.

45

Because of the steepness with which their layers pile up, strato-volcanoes have outlines of great beauty. The profile is concave upward, with gentle slopes near the base that grow steeper upward to the crater at the summit. Mayon, the most active volcano in the Philippine Islands, is regarded as the finest example of a strato-volcano. (See the picture on p. 142.) Many others the world over have similar graceful shapes, but perhaps the most famous one is Fujiyama, the sacred mountain of Japan, standing alone, 9,000 feet high. There are also majestic strato-volcanic cones in the United States—Rainier, Adams, Hood, Shasta, and others in the Cascade system of the Northwest.

Thus, according to the three groupings given above, all volcanoes may be described in three ways, according to recency of action, manner of action, and shape.

Craters vary greatly in size, and seem to have no proportional relation to the size of the mountain or its elevation. Haleakala, a volcano on the island of Maui, in the Hawaiian group, is 10,020 feet high and has a crater that is twenty miles in circumference; but Mt. Orizaba, in Mexico, is 18,200 feet high, and its crater is less than 1,000 feet in diameter.

The crater of an extinct volcano, after the volcanic vent has filled up, often becomes the reservoir for a lake. There are numerous extinct and even dormant volcanoes that have lakes in the old craters.

Sometimes lava builds up a conelike crater that is firm and strong for a time. This happens when the lava is so viscous that it hardens as soon as it rolls over the crater's edge, making a firm rim around the vent. Out upon this hardened rim more viscous lava rolls until a tall column is sometimes built which, in some cases, may stand longer than the rest of the cone. If the crater is large, this viscous lava may form a high wall or cliffs.

If the crater of a volcano is of great size and is shaped like a basin, or an open kettle, it is called a *caldera* (the Spanish word for cauldron). Most calderas are very wide compared to their

46

depth. In the Canary Islands there is a huge pit called La Caldera, from which other calderas are named. It is three to four miles wide, and is surrounded by a wall of lofty cliffs 1,500 to 2,500 feet high, except on one side where the encircling wall is broken down. As seen from a distance, the mountain resembles a huge cone cut off far below the top.

There are many calderas in the world. Some were formed by great explosions in which the tops of old volcanic cones were blown away, or else collapsed into the reservoir beneath, with only the resulting pits left to mark the sites of these wrecked volcanoes. In the terrific explosive eruption of Tomboro (see p. 140) a great part of the original volcano was blown away, and a caldera nearly four miles in diameter was formed. When the top of Mt. Katmai was blown off, a caldera was formed the rim of which may be clearly seen in the photograph on page 155.

Calderas are perhaps more generally formed by the sinking down of the column of magma in the chimney of the volcano after an explosive eruption. This leaves a great cavity under the cone, and the top falls down into the cavity. The edges of the cone that are left standing make the rim of the caldera. Such a caldera may be called, in simple terms, a "caved-in" crater. A caldera of this kind is occupied by Crater Lake in southern Oregon. A new cone grew up from later eruptions through the floor of this caldera, and is now an island in the lake on the site of an old parasitic cone. The caldera would appear as a great basin if it were emptied of the water now in it. (See p. 206.)

If the lava is too viscous to flow away from the vent, because of either low gas content or low temperature, it piles up around the vent forming a kind of dome sometimes called a "plug dome." Mt. Lassen Peak in California is a large plug dome, and within the Lassen Volcano Park there are thirteen smaller ones.

Erosion of volcanoes—A volcano is always subject to weathering and erosion. Even active and growing volcanoes usually have ravines and gulches down their sides. When a volcano becomes

47

extinct, the ravines are no longer filled up by materials from other eruptions, and the tuffs and breccia are carried away by wind and water. The hard lava flows and dikes give way more slowly, giving geologists opportunity to study their forms. In some parts of the world where there are no active volcanoes at all, geologists have found the old and hardened chimneys and volcanic necks through which the eruptions came in prehistoric times. Erosion has thus been of great service in revealing something of the internal structure of volcanoes; and in general, we depend on the work of erosion to supply man with answers to many questions that relate to the crust of the earth.

U.S. Geological Survey

VOLCANIC NECKS PROJECTING THROUGH THE HORIZONTAL SANDSTONE ON WHICH THE VOLCANOES ONCE STOOD.

This picture shows two large volcanic necks in the Zuni Plateau area of New Mexico. The more distant one is Cabazon. The mesa or tablelands in the foreground show horizontally bedded rocks exposed by erosion.

48

Professor Adolph Knopf, in *Outlines of Physical Geology* by Longwell, Knopf, and Flint, states very clearly this process of demolition: "As erosion progresses, the volcanic neck consisting of the material filling the central conduit becomes exposed to view. When the cone is demolished, the volcanic neck, because of its greater resistance, generally forms a conspicuous prominence; and, when erosion has finally swept away all external evidence of the cone and has revealed the foundation rocks on which the volcano stood, it remains projecting, a monument to the vanished volcano. Eventually it also vanishes, the 'roots' of the volcano become more and more deeply exposed, and finally all evidence that a volcano was once present, is obliterated."

5:

The Distribution of Volcanoes

There are probably between five hundred and six hundred active volcanoes in the world today; and those that are dormant, or but recently extinct, amount to several thousand. This is not surprising when we realize that volcanic activity on the surface of the earth has been going on for millions of years. Even during the present era of geologic time, it has been estimated that at least 500,000 cubic miles of volcanic rocks have been forced out upon the surface of the earth.

The great volcanic chains are situated on those belts of the earth's crust along which internal movements and disturbances have taken place. These belts are zones of weakness in the crust caused by fractures or folding or other movement, and have afforded favorable places for the rise of magma and its escape to the surface. The volcanic belts are also the principal earthquake belts of the world. These areas seem to be ocean basins, the territory bordering on such basins, or the range of mountains flanking the outlines of the continents.

The most marked volcanic belt on the earth's surface surrounds the Pacific Ocean, running along the western coast of South America through the Andes Mountains, up through Central America and Mexico, through the western part of the United States and Canada to Alaska. Then the line turns westward to follow the Aleutian chain of islands to Asia; then it turns southward through Kamchatka, Japan, and the Philippines, the Moluccas, the North Hebrides, New Zealand, and South Victoria Land. Enclosed within this somewhat circular belt are numerous other volcanoes, such as those on the Hawaiian Islands.

Another great belt extends east and west. From Central America it extends through the West Indies; then through the Atlantic by the Azores, Cape Verde, and Canary Islands. It runs through the Mediterranean, through Asia Minor and Arabia, and continues along the chain of the East Indies where it crosses the line encircling the Pacific and extends out into the Pacific Ocean.

It is estimated that three-fifths of all the active volcanoes in the world are in the Pacific Ocean. It is a remarkable circumstance that all the oceanic islands which are not coral reefs are composed of volcanic rock, and many of these oceanic islands, as well as other islands lying near the shores of the continents, contain active volcanoes.

The Pacific Ocean contains many submarine volcanoes whose ejected solid materials and molten lava never reach the surface, though they may have greatly disturbed the water. They seem to occur in lines and stand on ridges that rise from the floor of the sea. There are both active and extinct submarine volcanoes in the Pacific, and numerous volcanic islands that have grown above the surface of the water. An outstanding example is the ridge of Hawaiian Islands extending for 1,800 miles and crowned with mighty volcanoes, some active and some extinct. Many of the islands in the Pacific Ocean probably started as submarine volcanoes which reached the surface either by continued growth or by upheavals of the sea bottom. Both Vesuvius and Etna began their long geological histories as submarine volcanoes. Christmas Island in the Indian Ocean appears to be a volcanic mountain standing in water more than 14,000 feet deep.

Many temporary islands have been known to arise as a result of volcanic eruption. South of Sicily, where there used to be 100 fathoms of water, an island arose in 1831. Various discoverers claimed it and gave it different names, but it was better known as Graham Island. It finally grew about ninety feet high and nearly a mile in circumference; but while the ownership of the island was being disputed by the governments which claimed it, the island was growing gradually smaller by the action of the

51

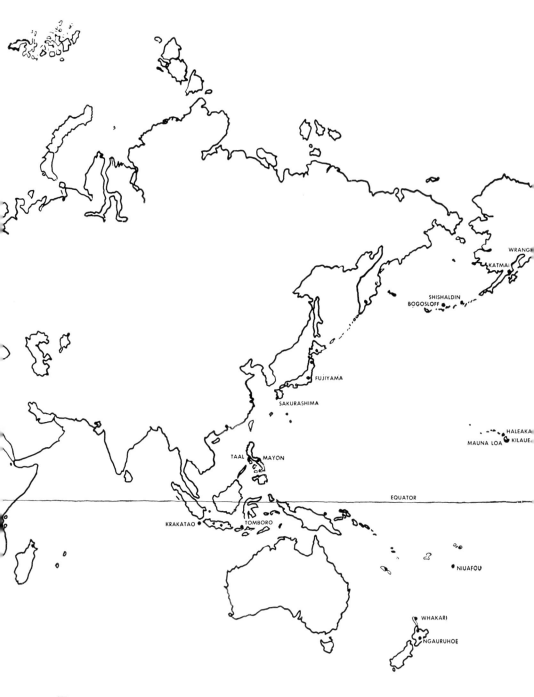

THE BLACK DOTS SHOW THE APPROXIMATE LOCATIONS OF THE BEST-KNOWN VOLCANOES OF THE WORLD, WHICH INDICATE THE MAIN VOLCANIC BELTS.

HEKLA · · ASKJA

· LASSEN PEAK

VESUVIUS · STROMBOLI · · ETNA

IXTACCIHUATL
PARÍCUTIN · · ORIZABA
POPOCATÁPETL
SANTA MARIA · SAN MIGUEL
IZALCO · · PELÉE
COSEGUINA · IRAZU · LA SOUFRIÈRE
MOMOTOMBO

NYAMLAGIRA · KENYA

COTOPAXI
CHIMBORAZO

VIRUNGA · · KILIMANJARO

· EL MISTI

ACONCAGUA

waves, and it finally disappeared. Thus the waves settled the quarrel by gnawing away the bone of contention. Other temporary islands have been noted among the Azores and the Aleutian Islands.

The American hemisphere has more volcanoes than the Old World continents. The loftiest volcanic mountains in the world are in the Andes of South America, some active and some extinct. A certain kind of volcanic rock is called "andesite" because of its characteristic occurrence in the Andes. Central America is rich in volcanoes, especially the republics of El Salvador and Guatemala. Also Mexico, which contains several that lie in a band stretching across the southern part of the country from west to east. Parícutin is on this line.

There is only one active volcano in the United States, Lassen Peak in California, but there are many extinct ones in the West. The Mississippi Valley is without any evidences of volcanism since ancient geologic times.

Much volcanic activity has taken place in Alaska and in the islands off the coast of Alaska. There are said to be fourteen active volcanoes in the peninsula of Kamchatka, and fifty-four (either active or recently extinct) in Japan. Fujiyama is the most famous one. There are several in the Philippines and in New Zealand. The Hawaiian archipelago has fifteen large volcanoes, but only two of them, Mauna Loa and Kilauea, are active. Java contains as many as fifty great volcanic mountains, active, dormant, and extinct. In the Straits of Sunda, the uninhabited island of Krakatao represents part of the basal wreck of what was once a volcano of gigantic size. A chain of volcanoes runs through Sumatra and the Indian Ocean.

Iceland is the most important of the Atlantic centers. From twenty to twenty-five volcanoes have been in eruption there since history began. Many Icelandic lava flows are from fissure eruptions. There is also a very important volcanic region in the West Indies.

54

Vesuvius is the only active volcano on the mainland of Europe, but in the Mediterranean Sea there are Etna, on the coast of Sicily, and Stromboli and Vulcano in the Lipari Islands.

The African continent contains active volcanoes on both east and west coasts, and others occur on islands close to African shores. On the continent of Asia more than twenty active volcanoes are believed to exist, the majority of them being on the peninsula of Kamchatka, and a few in Persia. In the center of the continent formed by Europe and Asia (the largest unbroken land mass of the globe), there rises from the great central plateau the remarkable volcanoes of the Thian Shan Range. At least three volcanic vents appear to exist in this region. The only accounts we have of the eruptions of these Thian Shan volcanoes are contained in Chinese histories and treatises on geography.

Until Parícutin was born, in February, 1943, the most recent volcanoes, so far as we know, were Novarupta and other smaller vents which arose in 1912 in a valley in Alaska (see p. 160), two in the Belgian Congo (pp. 169-170), and Chinyera, on the island of Teneriffe, one of the Canary Islands in the Atlantic Ocean. Chinyera was born in 1909 and, like Parícutin, is distinguished in having had eyewitnesses from the beginning. All of the new volcanoes of modern times have broken out in volcanic areas; none was born in an area that was not previously volcanic. From these facts it would appear that no part of the United States is in danger of a volcanic outburst except along the old volcanic belt in the West.

55

6:

A Few Other Volcanoes of Mexico

A MEXICAN DRAWING
IN THE CODEX TELLERIANO
REMENSIS—1509.

In an old Mexican manuscript of the year 1509, this volcano is pictured with its smoke and flames reaching the stars. In the original picture, the sky is blue, the stars are white, the mound is a dull green, and the curling central part is red and yellow. No indication is given of the name of the volcano. The translation of the old Spanish text beneath the picture is as follows:

"In the year 1500 on a very clear night which lasted forty days there were those who thought that they saw a New Spain which was very large and very resplendent, which was in the direction of the East and rose from the earth and reached the sky. In that year the people of Cocola, sixteen leagues from Huaxaca, rose against the Mexicans who attacked them and did not leave a soul, according to the old folks who were found among them.

"This [the above picture] was one of the marvels which they saw. They thought it was Quecalcoatle [the great white God] for whom they were waiting."

56

Pan American Union

POPOCATAPETL, WITH SMOKE ARISING FROM THE CRATER, AS SEEN FROM AN AIRPLANE.

Popocatapetl, several miles south of Mexico City, is the best-known mountain south of the United States. Its Aztec name means Smoking Mountain, and it is often called "Popo." It reaches a height of 17,880 feet. Its summit is always covered with snow, while bananas, palms, oranges, and mangoes grow at its base. The crater is about 2,000 feet in diameter, and within it is a small lake supplied by the melting snow. Steam still escapes from fissures in the bottom of the crater, and often there are soft wreaths of sulphurous vapor curling over the summit (as in the above picture), perhaps as a gentle reminder that Popo is only sleeping and may awaken at any time. Sulphur has been gathered from the crater by *volcaneros* for commercial purposes.

Pan American Union

IXTACCIHUATL ALSO RISES ABOVE THE CLOUDS,
AND ALWAYS WEARS A MANTLE OF SNOW.

Barely ten miles from Popocatapetl stands *Ixtaccihuatl* (Aztec name for White Woman), reaching a height of 16,960 feet. It is also known as The Sleeping Lady because the elongated, snow-covered summit somewhat resembles the form of a sleeping woman. The Aztecs thought of "Popo" and "Izta" as lovers who always kept within sight of each other. Ixtaccihuatl is older than Popo, and its crater has disappeared. It is considered to be extinct.

In southern Mexico the volcanic belt extends across the entire country, touching both the Gulf of Mexico and the Pacific Ocean. In this belt are both extinct and active volcanoes: Tuxtla, Orizaba, Cofre de Perote, Malinche, Popocatapetl, Ixtaccihuatl, Xinantecatl, Colima, Ajusco, Ceboruco, the famous peak of Tan·

58

citaro which supports 170 craters, and others. In fact, the craters of extinct volcanoes are scattered all over the southern part of the country. All the hills around Parícutin are of volcanic origin, and less than a mile from it lies a dead crater which geologists say was active thousands of years ago, but is now covered with vegetation.

Orizaba, the highest of these mountains (18,200 feet), is a beautiful and symmetrical snow-covered peak about seventy-five miles west of Vera Cruz. The ancient Aztec name of the volcano is Citlal-tepetl (meaning Star Mountain). There are three craters at the summit and they are usually filled with snow. It is known to have been active in the sixteenth century, but the last observed eruption was about the middle of the eighteenth century, and it is either dormant or extinct. Orizaba is surrounded by lava from its own eruptions. Two Americans who were connected with the United States Army which invaded Mexico in 1848 were the first white men to climb to the summit of the volcano.

Xinantecatl (Aztec name for Naked Lord; also called The Snow of Toluca) is about forty miles southwest of Mexico City, near the town of Toluca. In its summit there are two craters which form fresh-water lakes. The larger lake is thirty feet deep and contains fish of a peculiar species. Xinantecatl is not so old as Ixtaccihuatl, and its craters still remain; but it is also considered extinct.

Cofre de Perote, about thirty miles north of Orizaba, is 13,552 feet high with a summit that is quadrangular in shape. When seen from the Gulf, it resembles a sarcophagus, or coffer, which suggested its name. It is a volcanic cone that has passed its youth and has yielded, to a large extent, to the forces of erosion.

Tuxtla, a volcano on the east coast of the Gulf of Mexico about eighty miles southwest of Vera Cruz, is less than 5,000 feet high; but its small height is due to the fact that a violent explosion in 1793 blew off the entire top of the mountain and distributed its materials far and wide over the adjacent country.

This was one of the greatest volcanic outbreaks of modern times. Since then, less violent eruptions have taken place.

Colima, a magnificent volcano 13,000 feet high, on the west coast of Mexico, marks the western end of the volcanic belt that runs through Mexico, while Tuxtla marks the eastern end, so far as the land volcanoes go; but the internal line of weakness in the earth's crust probably extends beyond the continental line in both directions. Colima has been active during the last century, and lava was discharged during these eruptions, but nearly always from openings in the sides of the large cone. These smaller craters are called The Sons of Colima. It had a period of great activity for several weeks in 1903, resulting in a column of ashes that was said to be seventeen miles high!

In the peninsula of Lower California there are lava fields and volcanic mountains. At the north the highest summit is *Santa Catalina,* 10,000 feet high. Midway down there is a group of volcanic peaks called *The Three Virgins.* There were eruptions here in 1857.

Jorullo was born on September 28, 1759, in the midst of a cultivated plain. Many writers, probably relying on reports of the natives, have referred to it as a volcano that was upraised in a single night. No scientists were present during its first eruption, but fifty-six years afterward the great German scientist Humboldt visited the spot and gathered information from the natives who had witnessed it. Its first violence lasted several months, and eruptions continued for more than forty years. It filled the valleys around it with lava, and buried an extensive plain that had been occupied by fields of sugar cane and indigo plants belonging to the plantation of San Pedro de Jorullo. Earthquakes had frightened the inhabitants, who fled to the mountains of Aguasarco, and witnessed the eruption from these heights.

The first explosion blew out rocks, cinders, and other fragmental materials; clouds of steam and dust were emitted, and

AN OLD DRAWING OF JORULLO, WHICH WAS, BEFORE
PARÍCUTIN, THE YOUNGEST VOLCANO IN MEXICO.

lava flowed out. Four cones were formed, of which Jorullo, the
highest, grew to a height of 1,300 feet above its surroundings.
The four cones are shown in the drawing, with many small cinder
cones near them.

61

American Museum of Natural History

THE PEDREGAL OF SAN ANGEL.

This picture shows part of a hardened stream of lava which flowed from Old Ajusco, a now extinct volcano about 10,000 feet high, south of Villa Obregon in the suburbs of Mexico City. It covers many square miles and varies from twenty to fifty feet deep, according to the shape of the land over which it flowed. This lava flow took place at some remote period far beyond the memory of man, and scientists have dated it anywhere from 3,000, to 10,000 years ago.

The most interesting thing about this stream of dark, "frozen" stone is what lies beneath it. Only within recent years has it been known that this lava covered at least one, and perhaps several Indian villages. It had buried them more deeply and more securely than any known burial in the history of man, and left them under this enormous tombstone undisturbed for thousands of years. This important discovery was made because of the fact that the sides of the lava stream were used as a quarry for basalt

62

that was needed in the building of highways through Mexico. Several hundred feet back from the original front of the lava flow, in a quarry where the rock was being blasted with dynamite and removed for that purpose, the dynamite broke into this ancient sepulchre and revealed human skeletons and pieces of handmade pottery that belonged to what may have been the oldest culture on American soil.

It is easy to imagine the excitement of archaeologists and students of the early history of man when this gift of the dynamite became known. From studies of the pottery and figures that were found, archaeologists and paleontologists have dated these people as belonging to the archaic or the oldest historical level of America's inhabitants of which we have any evidence. Since no traces of architecture and no hunting paraphernalia have been found near them, it is supposed that the people were simple agriculturists.

In many places through this lava there are caves, cracks, and blisters which give the Pedregal (as this lava flow is called) the appearance of the moon as seen through a telescope. These weird cavities and dark hiding places had given rise to many tales of witches, ghosts, robbers, and bandits long before it was known that human remains lay beneath.

Near Copilco, at the edge of the lava, excavations have been carried on for several years, tunnels have been dug under the lava, and electric lights have been fitted into these tunnels. By the courtesy of the Mexican National Department of Archaeology, visitors may enter these tunnels and see human skeletons, pottery, and small clay figures lying in the exact positions in which they were caught when the red-hot lava rolled upon them, and as they have lain for untold centuries. The photograph above shows where the excavators are "crawling under."

7:

Central American Volcanoes

Courtesy of Ernesto Morales, Consulate General of Guatemala

THIS SILHOUETTE OF SAN PEDRO, IN GUATEMALA, WITH LAKE ATITLAN IN THE FOREGROUND, WAS TAKEN AFTER THE SUN HAD SET BEHIND THE MOUNTAIN.

64

Guatemala is rich in volcanoes that add much to the pictur-esque aspect of the country; but they are also a constant menace to the people who live near them. Their ashes, however, make soil of remarkable fertility, and there are many farms and coffee plan-tations on their slopes.

The volcanoes of Guatemala are not of the lava kind. They are bold, upstanding cones built up gradually of cinders and ash, with uniform sides sloping at an angle of about forty-five de-grees, as illustrated in the silhouette of San Pedro.

SANTA MARIA, NEAR THE MEXICAN FRONTIER, IS ONE OF GUATEMALA'S MOST BEAUTIFUL VOLCANOES, and is one of the most destructive. It is 12,361 feet high, and dominates the cof-fee lands of western Guatemala.

The most famous eruption of Santa Maria occurred on October 24, 1902. Ashes covered an area of more than 125,000 square miles; and in the region extending over 2,500 square miles, pumice stone and ashes fell to a depth of eight inches or more. Houses and farm buildings within this area were crushed under the weight of the ejected material, and in some cases they were totally destroyed. It is believed that six thousand persons were killed. The cloud from the volcano reached eighteen miles in

65

height, and the sound of the explosion was heard at Costa Rica, 500 miles distant. The entire side of the mountain was blown away, exposing an almost perpendicular cliff 7,000 feet high, and forming a crater three-fourths of a mile wide, seven-eights of a mile long, and 1,500 feet deep.

After this eruption, the coffee planters mourned their groves as lost; but later they dug down through several feet of ashes, and planted new trees in the original soil.

There were also disastrous explosive eruptions at Santa Maria in 1929.

U.S. Air Service from Pan American Union

A TRIO OF QUIET GUATEMALA VOLCANOES, ACATENANGO, FUEGO, AND AGUA, AS SEEN FROM THE AIR.

Volcan del Fuego (Volcano of Fire), in the center of the group, is about 12,000 feet high. It was in full activity at the time of the Spanish Conquest, and was probably active for a long time before that, since the natives at that time held it in great dread. During the sixteenth and seventeenth centuries it was less and less active, though in the following centuries its eruptions were frequent and terrible. In 1932 Fuego "blew its head off," spreading ashes over a radius of fifty miles.

66

Volcan de Agua (Volcano of Water), an extinct volcano, is not far from Fuego, and is shown at the right side in the picture. At the time of the Spanish Conquest, the crater at its summit contained a lake supplied by rain. In 1549, as a result of an earthquake, the wall of the crater gave way on one side, and an immense volume of water poured down the mountainside, carrying with it earth, rocks, and trees that lay in its path. It overwhelmed the Spanish capital that had been built on the lower slopes of the mountain, on the site where today stands the town of Ciudad Vieja. To the northeast of this old city a new capital was built, which is the present city of Antigua. In 1717, with an eruption of Fuego, came an earthquake that completely devastated that city. Again the capital was transferred—this time thirty miles away to the site of the present Guatemala City.

On a clear day one may see, from the summit of Mt. Agua, both the Pacific and the Atlantic Oceans.

Pan American Union

SAN MIGUEL, IN THE EASTERN PART OF EL SALVADOR, WITH CINDER CONES AND FERTILE FIELDS IN THE FOREGROUND.

67

The republic of El Salvador is the most volcanic country of all the Americas, and also the smallest, being about the size of Maryland. It borders on the Pacific coast, and is an important part of the "belt of fire" that girdles the Pacific Ocean. Within this small area there are four large volcanoes either recently or constantly active, and many others that seem to be extinct.

San Miguel is a regular truncated cone, rising 8,000 feet above the plain. At present it is inactive. Its most recent eruptions have consisted mainly of lava flows from the sides of the mountain, near the base. In 1848 several vents were opened about two thousand feet above the plain on the eastern slope and much lava was ejected, and also a small amount of ashes from the crater. An airplane view, looking down into the crater, is shown on page 45.

Lava currents radiate from this mountain for many miles in every direction, interposing vast barriers to travelers in approaching it. A large flow at the base of San Miguel is intersected by the line of the International Railways of Central America.

IZALCO IS CALLED "THE BEACON OF CENTRAL AMERICA."

68

Being near the coast, *Izalco* is visible from far out at sea, and the mariners welcome its brilliant flares. When it is in eruption, which is almost continuously, Dr. Rafael Gonzales Sol, writing in the *Pan American,* says that "its lava flows cover it from top to bottom, which at night give it the effect of a fantastic and colossal cone that is entirely incandescent." The people say that "the mountain bathes itself in fire."

Izalco first appeared in 1770, in what was then a fine cattle ranch. Without warning, the earth trembled and the crater opened, sending out a gigantic column of steam and a great quantity of lava and solid materials which began to pile up on the plain, and it has been almost continuously active ever since. Its cone is 6,000 feet high and is still growing. Every few minutes with a thunderous roar it hurls up an enormous geyser of white-hot boulders which come rolling down the slopes; then it stops for a few minutes, only to begin again with an almost exact repetition of its performance.

A strange thing about this volcano is that it appears to have no crater whatever. This puzzled volcanologists for a long time until it was watched from the top of a higher neighboring mountain, and the discovery was made that, during an eruption, the gases open the fissures for the lava, rocks, and other materials to be blown out, and when the eruption is over, the rocks apparently fall back to the edge of the opening and are promptly amalgamated by the falling lava which fills every hole, so that the summit remains, as before, without any crater at all until the next eruption blows it open again (Dr. Sol). In the *National Geographic Magazine* for November, 1944, is an interesting series of airplane photographs taken three seconds apart, during an eruption.

Izalco ranks among the most active volcanoes in the world, and has already discharged more lava than any other in Central America.

The volcano of *San Salvador,* near the capital city of the same name, until 1917 had been silent for over three hundred years, and was considered extinct. The crater, a deep bowl over a half-mile wide and about 2,400 feet deep, contained a lovely lake of lucid green color, and the water was tranquil and deep. At five o'clock on June 7, 1917, a series of earthquakes began which soon converted the city of San Salvador into a heap of ruins. Again quoting Dr. Sol in the *Pan American:* "At 9:30 o'clock there was a violent movement of the ground which made all who still stood lose their balance. Immediately the neighboring volcano was clothed with a tremendous sheet of flame, so enormous in extent that it seemed to fill the whole sky. This was immediately followed by a reverberating and continuous roar . . . and immediately there began to fall upon the inhabitants, already overcome with fright and fatigue, a burning rain of sand. The eruption took place in an exterior wall of the volcano's slope at a great height, near the old crater. But this new crater soon became obstructed, and there followed eruptions from the old crater which contained the lake. First the lake itself began to glow, an effect produced by the white-hot lava which burst forth from the lake bottom, but was unable to reach the surface because of the water's great depth. After a substantial portion of the water had evaporated, because of the internal furnace, there appeared in the middle of the lake from time to time, a black mass of lava which was again immediately submerged. Finally the lake was totally absorbed or boiled away, and the eruptions were openly seen. It became possible to watch them from the rim of the crater without any danger whatever. Strange phenomena were observable. First a little fissure at the bottom appeared, apparently about a yard in length and a few inches wide, and little flames emerged. Then there was a detonation like a broadside from a super-dreadnaught, and the entire mass of the volcano shuddered, while a great column of steam rose to the sky, forming a very high cloud. Amid the steam one could see fragments of lava of every size and shape. The largest pieces fell back from only a slight height, and then, broken and reduced in size, were thrown higher, the process repeating itself over and over until the smaller bits soared with the ease of rockets."

There have been, at various times, submarine volcanoes that grew until their heads came above the surface of the sea; but a volcano that rises from the bottom of a fresh-water lake is very rare. In 1879, Lake Ilopango, in the central part of Salvador, became the center of a violent earthquake, followed by rapid reduction of the water of the lake. In fifty-four days the lake's surface fell thirty-five feet. During the earthquake the lake was greatly agitated, and immense volumes of steam rose from its central portion. One night more disturbance than usual was noticed upon the water, and next morning a pile of rocks was seen in the center of the lake, from which rose a huge column of vapor. The eruptions continued for more than a month; the island of rocks increased in size, and from it rose continuously a vapor column fully 1,000 feet high. Meanwhile the waters of the lake became so charged with sulphurous gases that the fish, which had been abundant, all died. When the eruption ended, the island that had been formed was found to have an area of about five acres, and to consist of jagged black rock about 150 feet high. As this rock was shaped like a molar tooth, it was given the name of La Muela, which means The Molar. It stands in water about seven hundred feet deep. The region all about Lake Ilopango is composed of volcanic rocks, and it is believed that the lake occupies an ancient crater.

Pan American Union

THE CRATER OF COSEGÜINA, IN WESTERN NICARAGUA.

This crater seems peaceful enough now, but in 1835 it was the scene of one of the four or five greatest explosions on record. The summit of *Mt. Cosegüina* was literally blown away, and the rocks composing it were reduced to fragments and distributed far and wide over land and sea.

For two days, beginning January 20, 1835, explosions were heard three hundred miles away in every direction, followed by clouds of sand and dust. On the third day the darkness became intense and the explosions reached their worst. Sand fell continuously, and the people deserted their houses to escape the

72

danger of roofs falling from the weight of sand upon them. This sand and ashes fell several inches deep over an area 1,500 miles in diameter. On January 22, the noise of the great explosions was heard at Jamaica, 800 miles away, and at Bogotá, 1,100 miles distant, probably the second biggest noise of modern times. E. G. Squier, in his *Volcanoes of Central America*, reported that the superintendent of Belize, 800 miles away, mustered his troops under the impression that there was a naval action off the border. All nature seemed overawed; the birds disappeared, and the wild beasts left their hiding places and crouched, terror-stricken and harmless, in the dwellings of men. The people for three hundred miles in every direction were dumb with horror, and many believed that the day of doom had come. The brightest lights were invisible at a distance of a few feet, and occasional lightnings added to the terror of the people. This continued for forty-three hours, then gradually passed away.

During the eruption, no one could see what was going on because of the intense darkness, but later it became evident that a crater had been opened about twelve miles in circumference, from which vast quantities of lava had flowed into the sea and into the Gulf of Fonseca. The summit of the mountain had been blown into fragments, and the quantity of matter thrown out was incredible. The mountainsides were covered with rocks and fields of lava; sand and ashes had fallen to a depth of several feet for many miles around the volcano. The captain of a vessel which was passing along the coast a few days thereafter reported that the sea for fifty leagues was covered with floating masses of pumice, and that he sailed through it for a whole day without being able to distinguish, except here and there, an open space of water.

Since its great explosion, the rural population of that region has regarded Coseguina with fear and superstition; and some of them hold the belief that the volcano may be bribed into keeping quiet only by the sacrifice of a three-months-old infant into its crater every twenty-five years.

Three Lions

Momotombo, Which Victor Hugo Called "the Bald and Nude Colossus," Stands in Solitary Majesty on a Peninsula of Lake Managua, in Nicaragua.

Momotombo is one of a long line of volcanoes extending through the western part of Central America from Mexico to Panama. In western Nicaragua alone there are twenty-three volcanoes, and several of them are still active. Recently there was excavated, near the city of Managua, a section of solidified volcanic mud

74

showing deep footprints of men and animals that were fleeing from a volcanic eruption from one to five thousand years ago.

The eruptions of Momotombo are decreasing in frequency, and the volcano is usually seen steaming quietly, as the photograph shows. It is 4,125 feet high and has been climbed several times in recent years, though it is said that those who attempted to climb Momotombo in colonial times were never heard of again.

Three Lions

TWO CRATERS OF IRAZU IN COSTA RICA, SEEN FROM THE AIR.

75

Irazu has several craters, but the flow from these is mud rather than lava, and the wrinkled slopes of dried mud are clearly shown in the photograph. One of the highest craters is full of water at present, while steam escapes from a lower vent. Irazu is 11,326 feet high.

There was an important eruption of Irazu in 1723. The year 1910 was most notable for seismic activity in Costa Rica. On January 25 of that year the Poas volcano had a formidable eruption, there was a severe earthquake on April 15, and at the same time a new crater opened on Irazu.

On December 27, 1917, there was an unexpected eruption of Irazu in which showers of stone and heavy materials were ejected in great quantities; a column of mud was thrown up to a great height in the shape of a spout which, falling down, covered an extensive region. In 1919 black pillars of mud came from the cavity, one after another, wrapped in a dense, extremely black smoke. There were enormous quantities of stones that fell like showers of rain. Since then, the pillars of mud and showers of stones and ashes have been frequent.

Telica, northwest of Momotombo, and at least 500 feet lower, also steams continuously, and is probably Nicaragua's most active volcano.

Poas, another volcano of Costa Rica, is 9,508 feet high. Its crater contains a lake of steaming water that is constantly effervescing.

8:

Two Volcanoes in the West Indies

An eruption of *Mt. Pelée* on May 8, 1902, similar to the later one illustrated on the following page, destroyed the entire city of St. Pierre with its 28,000 inhabitants, but on that occasion no clear photographs were taken. This photograph shows very distinctly how the clouds of ashes and suffocating fumes swept down the mountainside, through the city, and on to the sea.

Until 1902, St. Pierre was the principal city of the French island of Martinique in the Lesser Antilles, and one of the most important cities of the West Indies, having a population of over 28,000. Many Americans were in business in St. Pierre. The whites were practically all French and Americans, the other inhabitants Indians and Negroes. This small island of Martinique had a share in French history as the birthplace of Empress Josephine, the wife of Napoleon.

Mt. Pelée rose several miles to the north of the city, a mass of dark rock some 4,000 feet high with jagged outline, and cut with gorges and ravines down which numerous streams flowed from the crater lake at the summit of the mountain. It was known to be a volcano, but Mt. Pelée was looked upon as practically extinct, though it had been in eruption as late as August, 1856. At that time no lava came from its crater, but it hurled out great quantities of ashes and mud with strong sulphurous odor. Then it went to rest again and slept until 1902. The people had long ceased to fear it, and no one expected that grand old Mt. Pelée, the slumbering old hill, would ever spurt forth fire and death. In fact, it was regarded as a sort of protection, and the natives had an almost superstitious affection for this mountain which was peace itself. These poetic people relied upon it to keep back

A. Lacroix

AN ERUPTION OF MT. PELÉE ON DECEMBER 16, 1902.

78

storms from the land, and with its stern brow to frighten the tempests from the sea. They pointed to it with pride as one of the most beautiful mountains in the world, and tourists climbed to the summit to enjoy the beautiful blue lake which sparkled in the old crater.

Not until two weeks before the eruption did Pelée show any signs of disturbance. On April 23 it first displayed symptoms of internal disquiet. A great column of smoke began to rise from it, with occasional showers of ashes and cinders. In spite of these signals, there was nothing until Monday, May 5, to indicate actual danger. On that day a torrent of steaming mud and lava burst through the crater and plunged into the valley of the River Blanche, covering the Guerin Sugar Works and killing twenty-four people. The mud which overwhelmed the valley followed the beds of streams toward the north of the island.

The alarm in the city was great, but was somewhat quieted by the report that an expert commission had been appointed by the governor of Martinique, and this commission had decided that the eruption was normal and that the city was in no peril. To allay the excitement further, the governor with several scientists took up his residence in St. Pierre. He could not restrain the people by force, but the moral effect of his presence and the decision of the scientists gave them confidence. The wife of the United States consul at St. Pierre wrote to her sister in Boston during the days of waiting:"My husband assures me that there is no immediate danger, and when there is the least particle of danger, we will leave the place. There is an American schooner in the harbor and she will remain here for at least two weeks. If the volcano becomes very bad, we shall embark at once and go out to sea."

But she and her husband trusted too long. They perished with all the inhabitants of the city on the fateful morning of Thursday, May 8. Were it not for the few who were rescued from the ships in the harbor, there would be scarcely a living soul to tell that

79

dread story of ruin and death. The most graphic accounts are those given by the rescued officers of the *Roraima,* one of the fleet of the Quebec Steamship Company trading with the West Indies. The vessel had left the island of Dominica for Martinique at midnight and reached St. Pierre about seven A.M. on Thursday. The greatest difficulty was experienced in getting into port, the air being thick with falling ashes, and the darkness was intense. The ship had to grope its way to the anchorage. Assistant Purser Thompson of the *Roraima* wrote:

"I saw St. Pierre destroyed. The city was blotted out by one great flash of fire. Nearly 40,000 people were all killed at once. Out of eighteen vessels lying in the roads, only one, the British Steamship *Roddam,* escaped; and she, I hear, lost more than half of those on board. It was a dying crew that took her out. Our boat, the *Roraima,* arrived at St. Pierre early Thursday morning. For hours before we entered the roadstead we could see flames and smoke rising from Mt. Pelée. No one on board had any idea of danger. Captain Muggah was on the bridge, and all hands got on deck to see the show. The spectacle was magnificent. As we approached St. Pierre we could distinguish the rolling and leaping of the red flames that belched from the mountain in huge volumes and gushed high into the sky. Enormous clouds of black smoke hung over the volcano. There was a constant muffled roar. It was like the biggest oil refinery in the world burning up on the mountain top. There was a tremendous explosion about 7:45, soon after we got in. The mountain was blown to pieces. There was no warning. The side of the volcano was ripped out and there was hurled straight toward us a solid wall of flame. It sounded like thousands of cannon.

"The wave of fire was on us and over us like a lightning flash. It was like a hurricane of fire. I saw it strike the cable steamship *Grappler* broadside on, and capsize her. From end to end she burst into flames and then sank. The fire rolled in mass straight

80

down upon St. Pierre and the shipping. The town vanished before our eyes.

"The air grew stifling hot and we were in the thick of it. Wherever the mass of fire struck the sea, the water boiled and sent up vast clouds of steam. The sea was torn into huge whirlpools that careened toward the open sea. One of these horrible, hot whirlpools swung under the *Roraima* and pulled her down on her beam end with the suction. She careened way over to port, and then the fire hurricane from the volcano smashed her, and over she went on the opposite side. The fire wave swept off the masts and smokestacks as if they were cut with a knife.

"Captain Muggah was the only one on deck not killed outright. He was caught by the fire wave and terribly burned. He yelled to get up the anchor, but before two fathoms were heaved in, the *Roraima* was almost upset by the boiling whirlpool, and the fire wave had thrown her down on her beam ends to starboard. Captain Muggah was overcome by the flames. He fell unconscious from the bridge and fell overboard. The blast of fire from the volcano lasted only a few minutes. It shriveled and set fire to everything it touched. Thousands of casks of rum were stored in St. Pierre, and these were exploded by the terrific heat. The burning rum ran in streams down every street and out into the sea. This blazing rum set fire to the *Roraima* several times.

"Before the volcano burst, the landings of St. Pierre were covered with people. After the explosion, not one living soul was seen on land. Only twenty-five of those on the *Roraima,* out of sixty-eight, were left after the first blast.

"The French cruiser *Suchet* came in and took us off at 2 P.M. She remained near by, helping all she could, until 5 o'clock, then went to Fort de France with all the people she had rescued. At that time it looked as if the entire north end of the island was on fire."

Careful inspection showed that the fiery stream which so completely destroyed St. Pierre must have been composed of poi-

81

sonous gases which instantly suffocated everyone who inhaled them, and of other gases burning furiously; for nearly all the victims had their hands covering their mouths or were in some other attitude showing that they had perished from suffocation. It is believed that Mt. Pelée threw off a great gasp of some exceedingly heavy and noxious gas, something akin to firedamp, which settled upon the city and rendered the inhabitants insensible. This was followed by a sheet of flame, probably caused by the combustion of hydrogen and other gases, that swept down the side of the mountain. This theory is sustained by the experiences of the survivors who were taken from the ships in the harbor, as they say that their first experience was one of faintness.

The dumb animals, with surer instinct than man, early took warning of the storm of fire which Pelée was storing up to hurl upon the island. It was said that even before the mountain began to rumble, late in April, livestock became uneasy and at times were almost uncontrollable. Cattle lowed in the night. Dogs howled and sought the company of their masters, and when driven forth they gave every evidence of fear. Wild animals disappeared from the vicinity of Mt. Pelée. Even the snakes, which at ordinary times are found in great numbers near the volcano, crawled away. Birds ceased singing and left the trees that shaded the sides of Pelée. A great fear seemed to be upon the island, and though it was shared by the human inhabitants, they alone neglected to protect themselves.

Of the villages in the vicinity of St. Pierre, only one escaped, the others suffering the fate of the city. The fortunate one was Le Carbet, on the south, which escaped uninjured, the flood of lava stopping when within two hundred feet of the town. Morne Rouge, a summer resort situated on an elevation between the city and the crater, was by great good fortune saved. The governor of Martinique, M. Mouttet, was lost. A few walls were left standing. The hospital clock was found intact, with the hands stopped at seven-thirty. The dead bodies were gathered up and cremated in large funeral pyres. Only four persons were taken alive from the ruined city, and of these, two quickly died and the third died very soon in the hospital.

In truth, only a single human being escaped from the city after the explosion in condition to survive, and he did so only after passing through a living death. This was Joseph Surtout, a Negro murderer who was locked in a cell so far underground that the gases, as well as the flames, failed to reach him. There he remained for four days before his cries were heard. During these terrible days he was without food and water—almost without air. He saw nothing, his cell being without a window, but he knew from the noise and heat that something extraordinary had happened. On the fourth day—though he had lost track of time—he heard voices, and shouted and prayed until he attracted the attention of the people. The cell door was broken open, and he dashed away like one crazed by his suffering. Though sadly shaken, he was physically strong. He had been condemned to death by human law for his crimes, yet of the many thousands who made the city their home, he alone was saved. (Most of the above is from accounts by Charles Morris in *Volcano's Deadly Work.*)

After the eruption had quieted down, a strange, black column appeared standing in the crater of Pelée, and remained for many months afterwards—a tall, chimney-like column of lava that was called Pelée's Spine, also The Tower of Pelée. It is shown in the photograph on page 84.

This photograph was taken June 13, 1903, at a distance of seven hundred to eight hundred feet from the crater's edge. "The aspect of the tower from this point," writes Angelo Heilprin in *The Tower of Pelée,* "with the steam and ash puffs and blue sulphur fumes playing about its base, was one of great magnificence . . . extraordinary obelisk of lava like a veritable Tower of Babel."

83

From *The Tower of Pelée*, by Angelo Heilprin, courtesy J. B. Lippincott Company

THE TOWER OF PELÉE.

84

It began to appear in August, 1902, though it was not then recognized as a pillar. It appeared and disappeared at first, frequently underwent decapitation, and the apex was frequently broken off and built up again. It first appeared as a "tower" on October 15, 1902, and in thirty-five to forty days after that, it had risen about 800 feet. There was frequent breakage, but continuous repair. At the time of its greatest development, it reached a height of nearly 1,000 feet, 5,020 feet above sea level.

This tower or "spine" has been variously explained. Some claim that it was formed, after the explosive eruption ceased, by very viscous lava rolling out over the ever narrowing crater's rim, and forming a tall "neck" such as was described on page 46. Others believe that this was an enormous plug of solid lava which had solidified in the throat of the volcano after some previous eruption and which, upon the explosion of 1902, became loosened in the ancient chimney and was thrust out in one long shaft by the pressure of the underlying gases and magma.

The systematic destruction of this great core of rock began in July, 1903. In two weeks it lost 400 feet, and disappeared in a few months. Heilprin says: "There remains little doubt in my mind that the tower of Pelée was merely the ancient core of the volcano that had been forced from the position of rest in which solidification had left it. . . . The power to lift, or even sustain, so gigantic a structure as this tower, with a cubical content equal to that of the Great Pyramid of Egypt, must have been prodigious."

The projection of the "spine" of Mt. Pelée, and the overwhelming flood of hot dust and gases that swept downward from the mountain, are features which make these eruptions very notable. Volcanologists have used this historic eruption as an extreme "pattern," and refer to volcanic eruptions as being of the *Peléean type* when dense clouds of dust and superheated steam blow out horizontally and rush down the sides of the mountain instead of going up.

For many months Pelée continued at intervals to eject these clouds; one of them which was ejected seven months after the great explosion is the one shown on page 78. The height of this cloud is 13,000 feet.

Twenty years afterward, St. Pierre had risen from its ashes and had 1,000 inhabitants. In September, 1929, ash eruptions began again from the crater of Pelée, and the authorities ordered a complete evacuation, but the explosions were mild, probably because most of the explosive energy had been released in 1902.

We often hear of "sympathetic eruptions" occurring at the same time in regions removed from each other, showing that there may be some connection in the internal disturbance. On the same day of the Pelée eruption, there was an eruption of similar type on the island of St. Vincent in the West Indies, ninety miles from Martinique. These eruptions of May, 1902, were followed in October by disastrous mud falls and floods from Santa Maria volcano in Guatemala. In like manner, the eruption of Pelée in September, 1929, was followed by disastrous explosive eruptions at Santa Maria.

A volcanological museum now stands among the ruins of the fated city of St. Pierre.

La Soufrière—St. Vincent Island is one of Martinique's neighbors in the Lesser Antilles group of the West Indies. On St. Vincent is a volcano called La Soufrière (The Sulphur Pit). This island and its volcano are of especial interest to us, for that portion of the island lying at the base of La Soufrière was occupied by the Carib Indians whom Columbus found there four and a half centuries ago, and for whom the Caribbean Sea was named. They had retained this part of the island as their special country.

La Soufrière's first eruption during historic times was in 1718, when lava poured from its crater; but the eruption of 1812 was

86

far more terrific. This came just thirty-five days after the great earthquake which hurled the city of Caracas, Venezuela, in ruins to the ground, and killed and buried 10,000 people in one minute. After a year of earthquake warnings, Soufrière broke loose on April 27, 1812.

A story is told of the first intimation of that outbreak being reported by a Negro boy who was herding cattle on the mountainside. A stone fell near him. Another followed. He fancied that some other boys were pelting him from the cliff above, and he began throwing stones upward at his tormentors, whom he supposed were concealed behind the rocks. (This calls to mind how Dionisio Polido tried to stop the volcano that was rising in his cornfield.) But the stones fell thicker—some of them too large to be thrown by any human hand. Only then did the little fellow awake to the fact that it was not a boy like himself, but the mighty mountain that was flinging these stones at him. He looked up and saw that the black column which was rising from the crater's mouth was no longer harmless vapor, but dust, ashes, and stones. Leaving the cattle to their fate, he fled for his life, while thunders of the mountain roared behind him as he ran.

For three days and nights this continued; then on the thirtieth a stream of lava poured over the crater's rim and rushed downward, reaching the sea in four hours. The great eruption was then at an end. Humboldt reported that on the same day the inhabitants of Venezuela and elsewhere, over a space of 4,000 square leagues, were terrified by subterranean noises which resembled frequent discharges of the heaviest cannon. At Caracas, as well as at Calabozo, preparations were made to put the place in defense against an enemy who seemed to be advancing with heavy artillery. But the internal thunder was only the signal of what was taking place on St. Vincent. With this great outpouring of lava from Soufrière, the earthquakes which for two years had shaken a sheet of the earth's surface larger than half of Europe were quieted.

The disastrous eruption of La Soufrière's neighbor, Mt. Pelée, began on May 5, 1902, and reached its climax on the morning of May 8. On May 6, Soufrière on St. Vincent's Island also began to emit clouds of steam with thunderous noises which terrified the people; but they seemed to be hypnotized, and only a few of the numbers who lived in the vicinity tried to get away. On May 7 Mt. Soufrière suddenly opened, sending six separate streams of lava pouring and steaming down its sides. Death was everywhere, and in its most terrible forms. Lightning came from the sky, killing many who had escaped the molten streams that poured into the valleys. Soon there were flowing down the sides of Soufrière hundreds of streams of lava which, uniting and separating, formed a boiling network from which there was no possible escape for any living thing that was caught within this net.

"For this great tragedy the setting was wonderful," writes Mr. Morris; "Soufrière literally rocked in its agony. From its summit a majestic column of smoke, inky black, reached skyward. The craters were vomiting incandescent matter that gave forth prismatic lights as it rolled away toward the sea. Great waves of fire seemed to hedge about the mountain top. Such thunder as has seldom been heard by man cracked and rolled through the heavens. From the earth came tremendous detonations. These joined with the thunder, all merged in an incessant roar that added to the panic of fleeing inhabitants. This lasted through the night, and the day and night following. On Thursday night a huge column so black that it had the appearance of ebony arose to an estimated height of eight miles from the top of the volcano. Ashes and rock, as well as lava, were carried skyward in this colmn to deluge the island and the ocean for miles around. Gradually the column mushroomed at the top and spread out into dense clouds that descended to bring night at noontime.

"The atmosphere was so laden with sulphurous gas that life was made almost impossible. Hundreds of those nearest to Soufrière were suffocated by this gas before they were touched by the burning lava. Many expected that the entire island would be destroyed, and the night of Thursday was given up to prayers. All that night the darkness was beyond description, save when everything was made light as broad day by the lightning that forked out from the volcano.

"Friday brought a little respite. Soufrière became less agitated. The lava streams did not decrease, but the showers of rock stopped for a time. Then those of stout heart ventured out to take stock of the wonderful ruin that had been wrought. All areas of cultivation were found to be destroyed, buried under banks of volcanic matter. Plantations and villages on the leeward coast were wrecked, and on five plantations, every vestige of human life had vanished.

"The entire district occupied by the Carib Indians was a smoking, incinerated ruin. Ashes were everywhere, being in no place less than two feet deep, and in some places lava had rolled over the deep banks of ashes. Every one of the Carib Indians seemed to have disappeared, there being no survivors known until some time afterward. All vegetation was destroyed. Not a sprig of green was to be seen on the island. Live stock had died. Houses had vanished from their sites. Rivers were dry, and their beds ran lava."

While the outbreak of Pelée on the island of Martinique killed more people outright, more territory was ruined on St. Vincent, bringing greater destitution there. The eruption of Pelée destroyed St. Pierre and its environs with their 30,000 inhabitants. Mt. Soufrière broke into activity at the same time and destroyed an estimated 2,000 on the island of St. Vincent. This includes most of the Carib Indians, which means the practical extinction of the tribe that was found on the island by Columbus. Only a small number of them remain on the islands of St. Lucia and Dominica. An old Indian prophecy that the Caribs would be sacrificed to the fire god which they worshiped was thus fulfilled.

89

9:

A Few South American Volcanoes

A SMALL SECTION OF THE MAJESTIC "AVENUE OF
VOLCANOES" IN THE ANDES, AS SEEN FROM THE AIR.

90

Nowhere else in the world are volcanoes so high and so forbidding as those of the Andes, especially in the region near the equator. All the highest peaks of South America seem to be of volcanic origin, and outflows of lava and tufa cover many of their sides and fill up the valleys between them. There seem to be countless numbers of cones and craters, some extinct and some still active, through Chile, Argentina, Bolivia, Peru, Ecuador, and extending into Colombia.

COTOPAXI, IN NORTH-CENTRAL ECUADOR, IS THE BEST-KNOWN OF THE ANDES VOLCANOES, AND IS THE HIGHEST ACTIVE VOLCANO ON EARTH.

Cotopaxi is situated less than one degree south of the equator. It rises 19,550 feet above sea level, but since the valley at its foot is 9,000 feet above the sea, it does not seem nearly so high. Its upper portion is a perfect cone 4,400 feet high, is perpetually covered with snow except near the crater, and supports several glaciers. The crater is surrounded by a circular wall of volcanic rock which forms a black coronet (appearing through a telescope like a parapet) above the grayish volcanic dust and sand which cover its sides to a great depth. Under this sand are snow and ice. The crater is 2,300 feet wide from north to south, 1,650 feet from east to west, and is approximately 1,200 feet deep. On the southern slope, at a height of 15,059 feet, is a dark, bare cone of andesite called Cabeza del Inca (The Inca's Head) with cliffs rising fully 1,000 feet. Accordng to tradition, this is the original summit of the volcano, which was blown off in the earliest known eruption. Deep layers of mud, volcanic sand, and pumice surround it on the plateau.

Cotopaxi is frequently described as one of the most beautiful mountains in the world, rivaling Fujiyama in symmetry of outline, but overtopping it by more than 7,000 feet. However, few are able to enjoy its beauty, as the summit is usually enveloped in clouds, and even in the clearest month of the year it is rarely visible for more than eight or ten days.

The earliest outbreaks on record took place in 1532–33, and since then eruptions have been numerous. Remarkable eruptions, spreading destruction over the surrounding plains, took place in 1698, 1738, 1742, 1744, 1766, 1803, 1877, 1885. The eruption of 1698 destroyed the city of Tacunga with three-fourths of its inhabitants, and other settlements. In 1744, its roarings were heard six hundred miles away. On June 26, 1877, a disastrous eruption from Cotopaxi devastated the surrounding country and destroyed the lives of 1,000 persons. There was also a violent eruption in 1903.

Photo by Panagra

BEAUTIFUL, SNOW-CAPPED CHIMBORAZO is one of the highest of the Andes volcanoes, 20,500 feet. It is now either extinct or dormant. *Chimborazo* is also in Ecuador, a country more subject to volcanic disturbances than any other in South America.

Mt. Sangay, just under the equator, was at one time considered the most active volcano in the world, and was called "The Flaming Terror of the Andes." It rises to an elevation of 17,450 feet in a perfect cone, with the upper 2,000 feet covered with snow. Its base is ribbed and scarred by the lava flows of centuries. They give support to the volcanic pile and resemble the buttresses of a Gothic cathedral.

Tungurahua, also in Ecuador, is called "The Black Giant," and is a constant menace to the surrounding country. Around the village of Baños, tremors of the earth and mysterious rumblings from the heart of the volcano are of frequent occurrence.

93

EL MISTI (PERU), FROM THE WEST, WITH THE CITY OF
AREQUIPA AND THE IRRIGATED VALLEY OF THE
CHILE RIVER IN THE FOREGROUND.

Arequipa is the third largest city of Peru, and is 7,550 feet above sea level, while *El Misti* is more than 11,500 feet higher than the city. Arequipa is considered one of the most beautiful cities in the world, "encircled by snow-fields and towers of rock." The buildings of this gleaming white city are made of sillar, a white, porous lava from El Misti which is easily cut into blocks and is very durable. Three volcanoes look down upon this city, Chachani, El Misti, and Pichu-Pichu, all of which have been silent for a long time.

El Misti is the youngest of the three, and is the only volcano in this part of the Andes that has kept its symmetrical form. Under the prolonged action of ice and snow, the others have lost their original shape. Columns of smoke are frequently seen rising from El Misti, but it has had no eruption since the Spanish Conquest, and we have no means of knowing how long it was silent before then.

Photo by G. R. Johnson, American Geographical Society of New York

THE CRATER OF EL MISTI FROM THE AIR, WITH AREQUIPA AND THE VALLEY OF THE CHILE RIVER IN THE BACKGROUND.

The photograph clearly shows the two craters, one fitting inside the other, the inner crater forming a collar of smooth lava inside the rough and partly destroyed cinder rim of the older crater. From the air, the smooth inner collar appears deep blue, with its interior a sulphurous yellow green.

Inside the crater were found, in 1677, the wood and stone remains of a small three-room building, the stones showing the form of the foundation. The wood of the structure must have been brought from a long distance, and it is believed that the building was used by the Indians for religious services of some kind to propitiate the god of the volcano. Harvard College established the Arequipa Observatory and Weather Station on the highest point of the outer crater in 1893.

95

On the boundary line between Chile and Argentina, in the southern Andes, stands *Aconcagua,* an extinct volcano about 23,000 feet high—the loftiest mountain in South America.

Calbuco and *Llaima,* in southern Chile, are the two most active volcanoes in that region.

OSORNO, IN CHILE.

Osorno rises between two lakes, Llanquihue (shown in the photograph) and Santos, which were once a single body of water, but are now separated by the long slope of lava, ashes, pumice, and gravel that were thrown out by Osorno long ago. The top third of the mountain is completely covered by a cap of ice all the year round, except in two places where the crater's rim of black, slaggy lava is exposed. Although there has been no known eruption of Osorno since 1850, there is still a small remnant of heat in the crater rim which keeps these two places in the rim free of snow, and keeps open caves extending down under the great heap of ice in the crater.

International News Photo

LAS YEGUAS SENDS LAVA, GAS, AND ASHES
OVER WESTERN ARGENTINA.

In April, 1932, four volcanoes of the Andes, *Descabezado* (which was long thought extinct), *LasYeguas, Tinguirica,* and *Zuizapu,* though many miles apart, broke into violent eruption at about the same time. In Buenos Aires, some seven hundred miles away, there was a steady fall of volcanic ash, totaling about three thousand tons, covering everything, and causing people to weep and cough. In the city of Mendoza ashes lay fourteen inches deep, and trains from Mendoza arrived in Buenos Aires covered with ash as if from a heavy snowfall. Even at Montevideo in Uruguay, over

97

eight hundred miles from the nearest erupting volcano, a rain of cinders came down. Over an area of nearly three hundred miles from Descabezado the air was almost unbreatheable because of sulphurous gas, and there was an urgent demand for oxygen drums. In the Mendoza province great cracks appeared in the earth, and plans were made for removing 80,000 people from the province, as coiling rolls of lava covered the mountains and the plateaus around them.

Ascension Island, in the Atlantic Ocean between South America and Africa, is an almost bare area of thirty-four square miles of volcanic rock. *Green Mountain* is a huge elliptical crater, and forty other cones of extinct volcanoes dot the island. In 1942, United States Army engineers carved out of this volcanic rock a landing field and refueling station which has proved very useful. A few British families now live on the island, but there are no native inhabitants.

10:

The Volcanoes of Hawaii

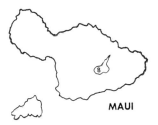

MAUI

The black areas show some of the lava flows from Mauna Loa. The numbers show locations as follows:

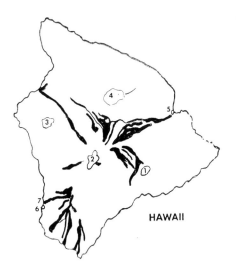

1.—crater of Kilauea.
2.—crater of Mauna Loa.
3.—crater of Hualalai (not active).
4.—crater of Mauna Kea (not active).
5.—site of city of Hilo.
6.—site of village of Hoopuloa.
7.—the Alika lava flow.
8.—crater of Haleakala (not active).

HAWAII

TWO ISLANDS OF THE HAWAIIAN GROUP, HAWAII AND MAUI, WHICH CONTAIN THE FAMOUS VOLCANOES.

These two easternmost islands of the Hawaiian group are probably the most interesting volcanic regions on earth. The volcanoes of Hawaii have furnished to men of science more knowledge of volcanology, and with the least destruction; they are the most frequently, variously, and harmlessly active of all the volcanoes in the world. They are truly a national asset, and a

99

volcanic eruption in Hawaii is cause for rejoicing rather than fear. Spectacular and violent as their outbreaks are, there is always plenty of time for observers to reach places of safety. There has not been a single death in the Territory caused by a volcanic eruption since the missionaries landed there more than one hundred years ago; and the only known loss of life from volcanic action in these islands was in 1790 when an explosive eruption of Kilauea destroyed a division of the Hawaiian Army.

The Hawaii National Park was created by an act of Congress on August 1, 1916, to conserve the most spectacular volcanic areas of the United States. It consists of two separate tracts of land, the Kilauea–Mauna Loa section on the island of Hawaii, and the Haleakala section on the island of Maui. These two tracts contain 275.71 square miles. Their craters, both active and dormant, may be approached with reasonable safety. An observatory and research laboratory are maintained at Kilauea, and also outside seismograph stations. Instruments so delicately balanced as to record the tremor of footsteps across a cement floor tell a permanent story of movements of the earth's surface, and especially that part in the vicinity of the active craters. The Hawaiian Volcanic Research Association was founded in 1911 for the purpose of keeping records of the volcanic activity in the Hawaiian Islands and around the Pacific Ocean. More than anywhere else, the science of volcanology has been fostered here, and the records thus far made at the Kilauea Observatory make up one of the most notable volcanological libraries in existence. *The Volcano Letter* is a quarterly paper giving reports of these records, and is published by the University of Hawaii.

All of the Hawaiian Islands are of volcanic origin. They are the summits of a gigantic submarine volcanic mountain chain rising from the bottom of the ocean. At a distance of thirty to fifty miles from the shores of these islands, the ocean is three miles or more deep, some of the mountains having a base of more than fifty miles in diameter on the ocean floor.

Mauna Kea (White Mountain) is in reality the highest mountain in the world, for it starts from a great plain on the sea floor, 18,000 feet below the surface of the water, and from a base only fifty miles wide it rises nearly 32,000 feet, its upper 13,825 feet being above the water. Mauna Kea's crater has disappeared, but at 13,000 feet above sea level, one of its old craters is occupied by a lake.

The island of Maui contains the great dormant (or possibly extinct) volcano, *Haleakala,* over 10,000 feet high; also the small extinct *Kukui,* only 5,780 feet high. Hawaii, the largest island of the group, consists of five volcanic mountains about twenty miles apart, but connected by saddles 3,000 to 7,000 feet high, formed by overlapping lava flows. The volcanoes on all the other islands are probably extinct, but Hawaii, being the youngest of the islands—and still "in the making" by volcanic action —has two volcanoes that are still active, *Mauna Loa* and *Kilauea.* The three extinct volcanoes on this island are *Mauna Kea* (13,-825 feet), *Hualalai* (8,269 feet), and *Kohala,* 5,505 feet high.

Haleakala means House of the Sun, and is derived from a legend about the Polynesian demigod Maui, who climbed to the top of the volcano, ensnared the rays of the sun, and forced it to travel more slowly in order that his mother might have time to complete her day's work.

Haleakala is now more than 10,000 feet above sea level, and was once a much higher mountain. Many years ago the dome of the volcano collapsed and formed a great crater with a circumference of twenty-one miles and an area of about nineteen square

CLOUDS FLOATING INTO THE CRATER OF HALEAKALA, ONE OF THE WORLD'S LARGEST DORMANT VOLCANOES, ON THE ISLAND OF MAUI.

miles, with walls over 2,000 feet high. All of Manhattan Island could be buried in this crater. Within these gorgeously colored walls lies a superb volcanic spectacle. Covering the floor are giant red, black, and orange cinder cones hundreds of feet high, and the lava flows between them are distinguishable by their variation in color as the work of different ages. From the rim of this great crater the panorama of cloud and mountain and valley, and the glories of sunrise and sunset, are unforgettable. Dr. T. A. Jaggar says that "the crater at sunrise is the grandest volcanic spectacle on earth."

© National Geographic Society—Photograph by Gilbert Grosvenor

CLIMBING TO THE SUMMIT OF MAUNA LOA AND CROSSING A
REGION OF SHINY SATIN-ROCK LAVA. THE SKY LINE OF
MAUNA KEA IN THE BACKGROUND.

Mauna Loa (Long Mountain) is the twin of Mauna Kea, being only 125 feet lower. Were it not for Mauna Kea's cinder cones (many of them indicated in the picture), Mauna Loa would be higher. Mauna Loa is an immense lava dome, not only the largest active volcano in the world, but in actual volume the largest mountain in the world. It also discharges more lava than any other volcano, and is called "The Monarch of Modern Volcanoes." It reaches a height of 13,700 feet above sea level, and, like that of Mauna Kea, its base reaches to 18,000 feet below the surface of the water—a tremendous turtleback 60 miles across and 200 miles in circumference at sea level. Although Mauna Loa is probably still in its vigorous prime, it has become so lofty that when the lava inside would escape, the liquid now finds egress from the flanks rather than from the summit crater, and these flows radiate in various directions from the mountain like the spokes of a wheel.

In describing the ascent to the summit of Mauna Loa, in the *National Geographic Magazine* for February, 1924, Gilbert Grosvenor writes: "A few miles further on we traversed a lumpy, rolling sheet of colored glass, extending as far as the eye could reach, glistening at times with the radiance of countless jewels, sparkling with the brilliance of diamonds and rubies and sapphires, or softly glowing like black opals and iridescent pearls. The hoofs of our animals broke through this satin stream with a crunching sound as if they were piercing the crust of frozen snow.

"Next we passed a perfectly symmetrical blood-red cone in a frozen jet-black shining sea of obsidian—a lovely sight—and a few hundred yards farther on, a red cone and a black cone side by side. An hour later we noted long tongues of brilliant red aa lava which had thrust across a field of yellow volcanic sand.

"The goddess of the volcano, like all vigorous savages, delights in strong, positive colors. Thus each lava flow sharply differs from its neighbors. As we crossed a jet-black flow of congealed lava, we skirted a bright red-brick cone, and in the distance clearly visible could trace the course of other flows in bronze, slate, pink and chocolate. The colors soften the sense of terrific desolation."

(Upon reaching the crater) "It was intensely interesting to behold the fountain head of the volcanic stream that had constructed the four great mountains forming the island of Hawaii —probably the most unusual group of volcanoes on earth. From our present knowledge, geologists are inclined to believe that when this spouting stream, which originated many miles down in the bowels of the earth, had raised Mauna Kea to its present height of 13,825 feet, it could force itself no higher and, being compelled to seek outlets elsewhere, formed Hualalai (8269 feet) and Kilauea. Then it transformed its energies again and erected Mauna Loa, the giant of them all."

104

National Park Service

THESE FOUNTAINS OF FIRE FROM MOKUAWEOWEO, SEEN OVER
THE HIGH WALL OF THE CRATER, ARE FROM
300 TO 500 FEET HIGH.

Crowning the summit of Mauna Loa is an elongated crater called
Mokuaweoweo, nearly five miles in circumference, with cliffs
around it from 500 to 600 feet high. This summit crater is very
active at times, with great columns of white-hot lava playing as
fire fountains several hundred feet high; but no flow has issued
from this crater within historic times. All historic lava flows from
Mauna Loa have been either submarine or have burst from the
sides at elevations of 7,000 to 13,000 feet. The major historic
eruptions of Mauna Loa are:

1873–74   A summit eruption of eighteen months' duration.
1877   A submarine eruption, one mile offshore.

105

1877   A major flow from the southwest rift, lasting for ten days.

1880–81   A flank eruption of nine months' duration. One stream of this lava flow reached the present limits of the town of Hilo.

1899   A flank eruption from the northeast rift.

1919   The Alika flow, from the southwest rift.

1926   A large flow from the southwest rift that destroyed the village of Hoopuloa as it reached the sea.

1933   A summit eruption. At this time airplanes were first used to take sight-seers over the eruption.

1935   The northwest rift produced a flow that threatened Hilo. The Army Air Corps successfully bombed the upper channels to divert it.

1940   A four-mile crack opened extending across the summit crater, with a gorgeous fountain display (see above picture) which lasted several months.

The Alika flow of 1919 from Mauna Loa—one of the tremendous outflows of the century—has been dramatically described by Dr. T. A. Jaggar, director of the Volcano Observatory, in the *Observatory Bulletin,* Vol. VII, No. 10, as follows:

". . . The horses were left at a high flow of brown block lava, and the walk to the source fountains was across some ten alternations of aa and pahoehoe. Here could be seen the line of rift cones, some forty cones visible at one time, a true fissure eruption, along a crack. Great fountains were spouting continuously along the fissure for a thousand feet, like a wall of red flames, and in detail they were seen to be made of incandescent, light, crumbly material, yellow when it shot up, and red when it came down. The noise was a roar like surf on the rocks, and was occasioned by gas rushing through a lava pool filling the rift, churning it to a foam, and flinging up the foamy matter as it fell. . . .

"Through the southwestern wall the lake had found an outlet, and here, in a gorge 40 feet wide, rushed the main lava flow, like the sluiceway of a dam. This flow, only 100 feet west of us, made

106

Hawaiian Volcano Observatory

"LIKE A WALL OF RED FLAME, GREAT FOUNTAINS WERE SPOUTING."

a fiery river, with current estimated 18 miles per hour. . . . The writer obtained one glimpse of the lake surface by climbing the rampart at the northeast end, where the summit was only 40 feet high and the fountaining less violent than at the south. The heat was intolerable, but by choosing a moment when the falling of fragments was at a minimum, it was possible to scramble to the edge, look in, and then beat a quick retreat. A definite lake surface of heaving, foamy lava lay about 20 feet below the edge. . . . It was at this lake that the Alika flow took its rise. . . . The stream plunged into the sea at the Alika shore over an older flow of the same sort some fourteen miles from the source rift. The stream continued to flow as a lava river for 10 days.

"The upward rush of steam where the lava made contact with the sea carried up rock fragments and sand, and built a black sand cone. . . . Great raft blocks of lava, red-hot or black, or

107

red below and black above, rode along with the current, either smoothly or rolling over, as though striking on the bottom.

"The color effects at sundown at the rift source on Mauna Loa were gorgeous beyond description. Over the scarlet fountains rose the sheets of red and green flame topped with lilac fume, against a murky green or blue-gray background. Above rose the great buff-colored volutes of cloud, with individual billows coffee-colored or brown. All of this was backed by an outer sky of deepest cobalt blue, with normal distant horizon clouds of pearly gray."

U.S. Army Air Corps

THE MONSTER DESCENDS UPON ITS VICTIM.
This picture of the village of Hoopuloa was taken from an airplane on April 17, 1926, twelve hours before the dark lava flow

from Mauna Loa buried the village, the harbor, and the wharf, on its way to the sea.

Not a single building was left of Hoopuloa. The destruction could not have been more complete if it had been a deliberate engineering enterprise. This flow of lava was 30 feet high, with a front of 110 feet. With its "tongues" pushing forward now here, now there, it advanced upon the village at the rate of three feet per minute.

"The main character of the advancing fronts from 20 to 40 feet high, is that of a caterpillar tractor," writes Mr. Jaggar, volcanologist in charge of the Hawaiian Volcano Observatory; "an upper layer of bowlders and gravel is rolled forward on a viscous red-hot paste inside, tumbles down at the front.in a debris slope, and this is eternally over-ridden by the advancing mass for which it lays the track. . . .

"It is interesting to observe in this picture the two ancient lava rivers right and left of the 1926 stream. It is the notch between their two deltas that has created Hoopuloa Harbor. It was the valley between their two heaps that guided the present lava flow straight down on the village which had unwittingly assembled its houses in this fatal lowland. Exactly the same lesson has been taught again and again by Vesuvius, and never has been learned. The lowlands and bays are attractive to the vinegrowers and the fishermen; but if they sought safety in a volcanic land, they would be compelled to rebuild in the ridges and the points of land."

Hilo, the capital city of the island of Hawaii, on the opposite side of the island, has been more fortunate. Twice within fifty-five years the city of Hilo has narrowly escaped destruction by lava flows from Mauna Loa. The eruption of 1880–1881, which burst from the flanks of the volcano, sent a river of melted rock moving toward Hilo for six months, varying in speed from fifteen miles an hour in the earlier stages to a few feet per day. It advanced thirty-five miles and covered an area greater than the state of Rhode Island, and several feet deep. It came so near to the city that the people could feel the fiery breath of the dragon in the city streets; and yet when it was within a scant half-mile of the gates of the city, it stopped, and "the great red dragon lay stiffened and harmless" only a few yards from the town. The native Hawaiians say that it was the Princess Kamahamena who saved the town by casting into the lava stream a lock of her beautiful raven hair which quickly appeased the volcanic stream.

Not so poetic was Hilo's later rescue. In 1935 the northeast rift of Mauna Loa erupted for the first time since 1899. This eruption came from an opening at an elevation of 9,000 feet, and another flow of lava from Mauna Loa's side was moving upon the city at the rate of a mile and a half a day, destroying everything in its path. On this occasion the forces of Nature were attacked by a fleet of United States Navy bombers who dropped 6,000 pounds of bombs from a height of 4,000 to 5,000 feet above the lava. By changing the surface and opening up new paths for the lava, its course was diverted, and the town of Hilo and the harbor were saved.

Photograph by K. Maeharo, from Longwell, Knopf, and Flint,
Outlines of Physical Geology, courtesy John Wiley and Sons

THE EXPLOSIVE ERUPTION OF KILAUEA IN 1924.

This was the only explosive eruption in the Hawaiian Islands since 1790, all other eruptions having been of the quiet type.

111

The cauliflower cloud in the above picture was considerably more than a mile high when the photograph was taken.

The crater of Kilauea is twenty-two miles from the crater of Mauna Loa, and appears to be an opening in the side of Mauna Loa at an elevation of 4,090 feet; but Kilauea is an independent volcano, older than Mauna Loa, and with apparently no inner connection, as their periods of activity have been independent of each other. The illusion of its being a part of the higher mountain is the result of a broad depression at its top, and of its gentle slopes, caused by lava flows from many lateral vents of both volcanoes, filling up the valleys between them. For this reason, Kilauea has no resemblance to a mountain, being a great cuplike depression on an extensive plain.

Within this depression is a vast pit in which red-hot lava rises and falls like mercury in a thermometer. The fury of this red, boiling mass of molten lava when it rages is indescribable; and it is appropriately named *Halemaumau*, The House of Everlasting Fire. Until 1924, this seething molten lava within the pit was usually visible at any time; but since then, its activity has been spasmodic. A few months before the 1924 explosion, the lake of lava in Halemaumau suddenly dropped and disappeared, and crumbling masses of rock from its sides fell into the smoking pit, choking the vents through which the volcanic gases had escaped. When the great explosion came unexpectedly a few months later, the tremendous blasts of steam cleared the vents and hurled boulders and ash thousands of feet into the air. The violent disturbances continued three weeks, by which time the fire pit had been enlarged to four times its former size, the opening being 190 acres in area and 1,200 feet deep.

From time to time this lake of lava has risen and fallen—its risings accompanied by brilliant fountains and inflows of liquid lava, and its lowerings accompanied by tremendous avalanches which send up enormous dust clouds.

112

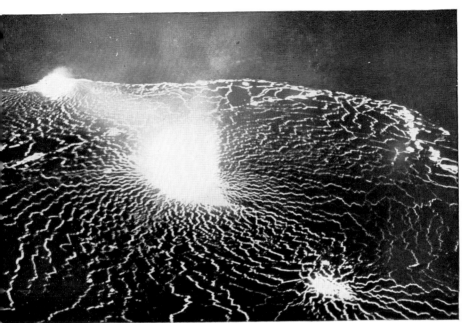

Hawaii National Park

A Night Photograph of the Lava Lake in
Halemaumau in the 1931 Eruption.

Following a series of earthquakes, molten lava broke into the bottom of Halemaumau on December 23, 1931, and furnished a spectacular display which lasted for two weeks. During this activity the pit was filled with lava to a depth of 100 feet, resulting in a new floor of 88 acres, which was 860 feet below the rim of the pit.

In the above photograph, the foaming fountains and the myriads of white-hot streams that radiate from them may be plainly seen. Halemaumau is at times a seething, roaring lake of fire, some 2,000 feet across; and again, a vast, silent hole 800 or 1,000 feet deep. Even in periods of normal activity, the lake with its islands and crags of solidified lava is most picturesque.

In the days of sailing ships, Admiral Charles Wilkes wrote: "The sight of Halemaumau was magnificent and worth a voyage around the world to witness."

113

Underwood-Stratton

An Island of Previously Hardened Lava Some Two City Blocks in Area Struggles with Another Oncoming Flow.

Underwood-Stratton

Gone! The Lava Lake of Halemaumau Has Completely Engulfed the Island Shown in the Previous Picture.

114

© National Geographic Society—Photograph by C. S. Carlsmith

RED-HOT "CREEPING TOES" OF PAHOEHOE LAVA SLOWLY
SPREADING OVER THE FLOOR OF HALEMAUMAU, KILAUEA'S
"HOUSE OF EVERLASTING FIRE."

The interesting formation of the walls of the fire pit are clearly
shown here. On the rim of the crater, far above this view, is situated the famous Volcano Observatory for the study of volcanoes
and earthquakes.

Scientists are indebted to the Hawaiian language for the terms
to distinguish the two different kinds of lava. One type, resembling rough clinkers or slag from a furnace, is named *aa;* the
other type, which is smooth and shiny glass, is known as *pahoehoe,* often called "satin-rock."

115

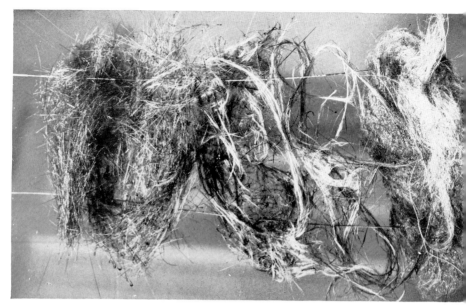

FINELY SPUN LAVA KNOWN AS "PELE'S HAIR" IN MEMORY OF THE HAWAIIAN GODDESS OF THE VOLCANOES.

Above the seething lava of Halemaumau, the air is sometimes filled with gossamer threads of glass which are carried away by the wind and accumulate in large quantities on the adjacent cliffs. This "Pele's Hair" furnishes a convenient and suitable material with which birds build their nests.

The goddess Pele, with her sisters and a brother, were reported to have come from Samoa in ancient times, and settled in the island of Hawaii. The cones within the craters of the volcanoes were their houses, and when the craters roared and flamed, the goddesses were supposed to be dancing. The ancient Hawaiians sometimes threw the bodies of relatives into a crater, in order that they might join the company of the deities, who would afterward befriend the family. Whenever there was an eruption in Hawaii in the olden days, the people would pick ohele berries and throw them into the crater as an offering to Pele. They also sacrificed pigs, for pork was supposed to be a favorite dish of the goddess.

11:

In the South Seas

Niuafou is a volcanic island in the South Pacific Ocean, between Samoa and the Fiji Islands. No mountainous form is seen in the photograph, for the volcano rests on the floor of the ocean, and only the rim of its crater extends above the surface of the water, forming this island. Within the crater is a lake; and the crater rim around the lake makes almost a perfect ring, which gives the island the appearance of a coral atoll. It has been called Tin Can Island because formerly mail was delivered in tin cans from the outside world to this island.

Niuafou is occupied by one of the Polynesian tribes, the Tongans, who have dwelt within this crater for untold generations, and none of the threats of Nature makes them consider leaving it.

In some of the South Sea Islands volcanic action has been frequent, and the natives have learned to act swiftly when the danger signals are seen. Dr. Jaggar relates how, on June 25, 1925, the villagers of Futu, on the island of Niuafou, were awakened at four A.M. by a rumbling, and saw fire breaking out on the hillside two miles away. By eight A.M. nearly all the buildings in the village were burned and buried under great floods of lava which flowed over them and into the sea. But all of the inhabitants of the village were saved by their swift and shrewd action. From the moment they were awakened they lost no time in spreading the alarm through the village, and quickly carried their children, the sick, and the aged away to the village of Angaha on a high ridge of the island's circular ring.

Niuafou Island is also the site of the unfortunate village of Ahua, which, according to the legend, was founded by men and

117

U.S. Navy Official

AN ERUPTION ON NIUAFOU OR "TIN CAN" ISLAND.

118

women who rebelled against the strict laws governing legal marriage imposed by the high chief of Angaha. They founded their village on the opposite side of the island, and also denounced the taxes which the high chief imposed upon them. Their headman spoke against this tax with heated oratory, and called upon the gods to send a sign from heaven to destroy all his people rather than permit them to pay this tax. It is known that "On June 24th, 1853, the ground opened, and lava spouted up directly under the village headman's house. There were earthquakes and rumblings. The crack extended lengthwise of the village street, and the fiery slag spouted up and flowed down to the sea. Presumably the eruption was at night, for the headsman and many of the natives were trapped and burned. The village was destroyed and two-thirds of its population (over 60 or 70 people) were killed." Such destruction of human life by sudden lava flow is unusual, for lava is usually so slow-moving that people have time to flee from it.

The highest point of the Niuafou crater is about 800 feet above the water, but the volcano has built itself up from the ocean floor some 6,000 feet below. There seems to be some form of volcanic sympathy between Niuafou and Tarawera volcano, in New Zealand, whose great eruption occurred only two months before an eruption of Niuafou. These craters are hundreds of miles apart, but they are situated on the same general rift in the earth's crust.

The outbreak of August 31, 1886, was a memorable event in the history of Niuafou. After a terrific earthquake, huge cauliflower clouds of sand and dust arose; but fortunately the trade winds forced them westward away from the settlements, and no lives were lost. Heaps of sand were piled up two hundred to four hundred feet high, and three feet of ash fell on the settlements. First, there was an earthquake at seven P.M. (on August 31); then at midnight, according to Jaggar, "there came a detonation, and a rocket ascended 3,000 feet above the lake, and the quaking

119

ceased. Violent thunderstorms developed, and lightning struck in many places. A blizzard of black dust and sand weighted down the vegetation during a night of inky darkness. On the leeward side of the island, broken fragments of rock and pumice, along with sand and fine dust, piled 20 feet deep. The eruption continued in spasms, geyserlike, for 18 days, with recurrences of terrifying clouds of dust that shut off the light of day." (From "Living on a Volcano" by Thomas A. Jaggar, in *National Geographic Magazine*, July, 1935.)

In 1919 another eruption of the Niuafou crater destroyed about four thousand acres of cocoanut plantations and ten thousand dollars' worth of traders' property, but the natives are still content to remain. The convulsion of the island as shown in the photograph above took place in 1943.

12:

New Zealand

NGAURUHOE, THE ONLY ACTIVE VOLCANO IN NEW ZEALAND. This is one of three volcanoes in the *Tongariro National Park*. The Maori tribes who held the ancestral title to this country made it possible through their generous gift to dedicate this land as a playground for the people of New Zealand. *Ngauruhoe* shows signs of eruption only at intervals of three or four years; the eruptions are not violent, and the lava flow is small. Before an eruption there is always a warning by a large column of smoke which rises to tremendous heights, and is frequently lit by brilliant flashes of light from the crater.

The two other volcanoes in the park are *Ruapehu* and *Tongariro*. Tongariro has been inactive for a number of years, and Ruapehu is also more or less extinct. Its crater is filled with a beautiful green lake warm enough in places for climbers to bathe in, in spite of the perennial ice right up to the edge.

The greatest volcanic eruption in New Zealand within recent times was in 1886 when *Mt. Tarawera* was split in two. A fissure some eight miles long opened with about twenty new craters which erupted an immense amount of fragmentary material. Showers of ashes covered an area of 4,000 square miles. This eruption destroyed the famous pink and white terraces on Lake Rotomahana.

Down the side of Mt. Tongariro flows a warm stream containing large amounts of chemicals which seem to be slowly forming colored terraces such as those that Tarawera destroyed, or perhaps like those of the Yellowstone National Park.

New Zealand Legation

MT. EGMONT IS CONSIDERED ONE OF THE MOST BEAUTIFULLY SHAPED MOUNTAINS IN THE WORLD.

Mt. Egmont is another extinct volcano in the North Island of New Zealand. Its lower slopes are covered with glorious virgin bush through which race cold, clear, snow-fed streams. Its cap is always covered with snow, and throughout most of the year there is a halo of cloud around the mountain hanging about two hundred feet below the summit, making the snow-covered peak appear to be suspended in the air. The peak is 8,260 feet above sea level.

There is a very old Maori legend that originally there were four mountain peaks in the area which is now the Tongariro National Park, but that the fourth, Mt. Egmont, became involved in a quarrel with the other three, and was buffeted so strongly by Mt. Ruapehu that he rolled back across the country until he reached the sea at what is now Cape Egmont.

123

Frank Stewart

THE VOLCANIC ISLET OF WHAKARI, OR "WHITE ISLAND," is forty miles off the northeast coast of North Island, in the Bay of Plenty. *Whakari*, the name given it by the New Zealand Maoris, means "suspended from heaven by a white cloud." They thought it could not come from the sea bottom because the ocean here is five to seven miles deep. However, it is a deep-sea volcano, with only its head above the surface. The famous world navigator, Captain Cook, was the first white man to see this volcano. He apparently saw it immediately after one of its eruptions, in which it throws up huge quantities of gypsum. This white material covers the entire peak and resembles snow when seen from a distance, and Captain Cook gave it the name *White Island*.

Molten Sulphur flows from the crater into the sea, discoloring the water. Sulphur works were established on the island for the extraction of sulphur from the volcano. Its last big eruption was in 1914, when it swallowed up all the employees of the sulphur works, and only a pet cat lived through that dreadful night.

124

New Zealand Legation

THE WALMANGU GEYSER AT ROTORUA.

Some parts of the volcanic districts of North Island have entered the dying stage of the volcanic cycle. The main activity has largely ceased; but hot springs, geysers, steam jets, and mud volcanoes still remain as signs of dying volcanicity.

125

New Zealand Legation

BOILING MUD IN NORTH ISLAND WHICH INDICATES THE DYING VOLCANICITY OF THAT REGION.

126

13:

The Volcanic East Indies

Java, a part of the Netherlands Indies, with its 45,000,000 inhabitants, is the most densely populated area of its size on the globe. It is distinguished for its many highly active and destructive volcanoes which, since 1500 A.D., have ejected more fragmentary material than the volcanoes of any other country. Of its 125 volcanoes at least 13 are active, and some of these are constantly in eruption.

Papandayan, with its green sulphur deposits, is one of the most picturesque of Java's burning mountains, about 8,750 feet high. There was a famous eruption of this volcano in 1772. For some time previous to the eruption it had been constantly sending out steam and smoke, but as no harm was done, the natives continued to live on its sides. Suddenly this enormous mountain fell in, and left a gap fifteen miles long and six miles broad. Enormous quantities of material were thrown out—even more than were thrown out by Krakatao in 1883. Forty villages were destroyed, some carried down and others buried by mud and lava. Some of the towns buried under the ejected materials were at long distances from the mountain. About 3,000 people, vast numbers of cattle, and most of the coffee plantations in the neighboring districts were destroyed. The volcano was reduced in height from 9,000 to 5,000 feet.

Even more terrible was the eruption of *Mt. Salek,* another volcano of Java. The burning mountain was seen one hundred miles away, and the thunders of its convulsions and tremblings of the earth reached even farther. Seven hills, at whose base ran a river—crowded with dead buffaloes, deer, apes, tigers, and

Royal Dutch Air Lines—K.L.M.

TJERIMAI, ONE OF JAVA'S MANY ACTIVE VOLCANOES, RISES
9,000 FEET ABOVE SEA LEVEL IN THE CENTRAL
PART OF THE ISLAND.

crocodiles—slipped down and became a level plain. River courses were changed, forests were burned up, and the whole face of the country was completely altered.

Another volcano, *Galung Gung,* previous to 1822 was covered from top to bottom with a dense forest, and around it were populous villages. The mountain was high, and on the top of its cone was a slight hollow, a basin-like valley carpeted with green.

128

In July, 1882, this tranquil peacefulness came to an end; one of the rivers became muddy and its waters grew hot. In October without any warning, a terrific explosion was heard; the earth shook and immense columns of hot water, boiling mud mixed with burning brimstone, ashes, and stones was hurled upward from the top of the mountain like a waterspout. This material was thrown out with such wonderful force that great quantities of it fell forty miles away. Every valley near the mountain became filled with burning torrents; the rivers, swollen with hot water and mud, overflowed their banks and swept away the escaping villagers along with the bodies of cattle, wild beasts, and birds which were carried down the flooded streams. Between the mountain and a river forty miles away, a space of twenty-four miles was covered with such a depth with blue mud that people were buried in their houses, and not a trace of the numerous villages and plantations could be seen. The boiling mud and cinders were thrown out from the crater with so much violence that, while many distant villages were utterly destroyed and buried, others much nearer the volcano were scarcely injured. All of this took place in only five hours.

Four days later a second eruption occurred, even more violent than the first. Mud and masses of slag (like basalt) fell seven miles away, and a violent earthquake shook the whole district. The entire top of the mountain fell in, and so did one of its sides, leaving an enormous gaping chasm. Hills appeared where before there had been level land, and the rivers changed their courses, drowning 2,000 people in one night. At some distance from the mountain a river runs through a large town, and the first intimation the inhabitants had of all this horrible destruction was the news that the bodies of men and the carcasses of stags, rhinoceroses, tigers, and other wild animals were rushing with the river down to the sea. No less than 114 villages were destroyed, and more than 4,000 persons were killed by this terrible catastrophe. (From the account given by Morris.)

A GROUP OF JAVA'S VOLCANOES, SEEN FROM THE AIR.
Semeru, the largest of the Javanese volcanoes, is more than 12,-
000 feet high; but quietly steaming *Bromo,* only the crater of
which is seen above the clouds in the picture, is only about 7,800
feet high.

In 1919 the volcano *Keluit* broke out after being dormant for
eighteen years. A crater lake had been formed at the summit
during this quiet interval, and now its waters rushed down the
valleys, killing 5,500 people. Since then a tunnel has been
driven into the crater, draining the lake and making impossible

a repetition of this particular form of volcanic disaster.

Mt. Merapi in Java has also taken a large death toll. In 1931, an eruption from this volcano caused the loss of 1,300 lives. A copious rain of ashes descended on the surrounding country, while there poured from the crater a stream of lava more than four miles long, two hundred yards wide and eighty feet high, bringing great destruction to that locality.

In Sumatra there is a volcano with a very similar name—*Mt. Marapi*—which is shown in the following picture.

K.P.M. Lines

A RICE VILLAGE IN THE MINANGKABAU DISTRICT OF SUMATRA. Marapi volcano rises in the background, and fields of rice occupy the foreground. Notice the unique architecture of the village.

131

Off the coast of Java, in the Sunda Strait between Java and Sumatra, lies what is left of the volcanic island of *Krakatao*. Until 1883 few had ever heard of Krakatao. The people of Java and Sumatra used to draw their canoes upon its beach and leave them while they searched for wild fruits. The island was known to have been of volcanic origin, but there had been no outbreak for 200 years, so it was regarded as extinct.

On May 20, 1883, "booming sounds like the firing of artillery" were heard at Batavia, in Java, one hundred miles away. Next day the captain of a vessel passing through the Strait of Sunda saw that Krakatao was in eruption. The smoke was estimated to have reached a height of seven miles, while the volcanic dust drifted as far as three hundred miles. The volcano continued to play with varying activity for about fourteen weeks. Then suddenly came the great explosion.

As the island was not inhabited, no one actually saw what took place. Those nearest to the scene of the eruption had enough to do to save their own lives, while the clouds of vapor dust were so dense that the volcano was completely hidden. This phase of greatest violence started on Sunday, August 26. Soon after midday, sailors on passing ships saw that the island had vanished behind a dense cloud of black vapor which was estimated to be not less than seventeen miles in height. Frightening sounds were heard at intervals, and after a time a rain of pumice began to fall at places ten miles away, while fierce flashes of lightning rent the vapor. These disturbances grew more and more alarming until next day when four explosions of fearful intensity shook the earth and sea and air. The third explosion was by far the most violent and productive of the most widespread results. It was, perhaps, the most tremendous volcanic outburst in intensity known in human history. After this great explosion the eruption declined, and in a day or two it practically died away.

The eruption spread ruin and death over many surrounding leagues. When men once more reached the shores of Krakatao

132

Underwood and Underwood

THIS EXPLOSION ON THE ISLAND OF KRAKATAO TOOK PLACE
FIFTY YEARS AFTER THE MOST TREMENDOUS
ERUPTION OF MODERN TIMES.

133

itself, everything was found to be changed. About two-thirds of the main island was completely blown away. The volcanic cone was cut nearly in half vertically, the new cliff falling straight down toward the center of the crater. Where land had been before, there now was the sea, in some places more than one hundred feet deep. But the part of the island that remained had been somewhat increased by ejected materials. Of the other islands and islets, some had entirely disappeared and some were partly destroyed; others were enlarged by fallen debris, while many changes had taken place in the depth of the neighboring sea bed. Two new islands (Steers and Calmeyer) were formed.

The ejected pumice was so full of large holes that it floated upon the water, and at places formed great floating islands which covered the sea for miles and sometimes rose from four to seven feet above it, proving a serious obstacle to navigation. The enormous clouds of volcanic dust which had been hung high into the air darkened the sky for a great area around. At Batavia, about one hundred miles from the volcano, the dust produced an effect much like that of a London fog. Lamps were required in the houses, and by noon a downfall of rain, mingled with the dust, put the town in complete darkness. Dust fell to a depth of eighteen inches on the vessels near the island.

Following the eruption a succession of enormous waves, starting from Krakatao and traversing the sea, swept the coasts that bordered the Strait of Sunda with such tremendous force that it destroyed many villages on the low-lying shores in Java, Sumatra, and other islands. Buildings that were fifty feet above sea level were washed away, and in some places the water rose higher —in one place reaching the height of 115 feet. At Telok Betong, in Sumatra, a ship was carried inland for a distance of nearly two miles and left stranded at a height of thirty feet above sea level.

The eruption of Krakatao seems to have formed an internal convulsion that affected many of the volcanoes of Java, which broke into violent eruption at almost the same time. Dr. Bonney states that "The disturbances originated on the island of Krakatao with eruptions of red-hot stones and ashes; and by noon next day, Semeru, in Java, was reported to be belching forth flames at an alarming rate. The eruption soon spread to Gunung Guntur and other mountains, until more than a third of the 45 craters of Java were either in activity or seriously threatening it. . . . The volcanoes in the Kedang range, and the volcano of Papandayan were in violent eruptions. A whirlwind accompanied the eruptions by which house-roofs, trees, men and horses were swept into the air."

All along the coasts of the adjoining islands, towns and villages were swept away and their inhabitants drowned. The total loss was, as nearly as could be estimated, 36,000 souls.

The distant effects of this explosion were as remarkable as the near ones. The concussion of the air reached to an unprecedented distance and the clouds of floating dust encircled the earth, producing striking phenomena. This historic event is so important that it seems worth while to quote at length from a well-known English authority, Sir Robert Ball, who says in *Earth's Beginnings* (1902):

"By 10 A.M., August 27th, 1883, the rehearsals were over and the performance began. An overture, consisting of two or three introductory explosions, was succeeded by a frightful convulsion which tore away a large part of the island of Krakatao and scattered it to the winds of heaven. In that final onthrust all records of previous explosions on this earth were completely broken. It was this supreme effort which produced the mightiest noise that, so far as we can ascertain, has ever been heard on this globe. . . . It has been proved by evidence which cannot be doubted that the thunders of the great volcano attracted the attention of an intelligent coast-guard on the island of Rodriguez [nearly 3,000 miles away] who carefully noted the character of the sounds and the time of their occurrence. He had heard them just four hours after the actual explosion, for this is the time

135

the sound occupied on its journey. [If such an explosion had occurred on Pike's Peak, it might have been heard all over the United States.]

"This mighty incident at Krakatao has taught us another lesson on the constitution of our atmosphere. We previously knew almost nothing as to the conditions prevailing above the height of ten miles overhead. It was Krakatao which gave us a little information which was greatly wanted. How could we learn that winds were blowing at a height four times as great as the loftiest mountain on earth, and twice as great as the loftiest altitude to which a balloon has ever soared? . . . There was nothing to render the winds perceptible until Krakatao came to our aid. Krakatao drove into those winds prodigious quantities of dust. Hundreds of cubic miles of air were thus deprived of that invisibility which they had hitherto maintained.

"With eyes full of astonishment men watched those vast volumes of Krakatao's dust on a tremendous journey. Of course everyone knows of the so-called trade-winds on our earth's surface which blow steadily in fixed directions, and which are of such service to the mariner. But there is yet another constant wind. It was first disclosed by Krakatao. Before the occurrence of that eruption, no one had the slightest suspicion that far up aloft, 20 miles over our heads, a mighty tempest is incessantly hurrying with a speed much greater than that of the most awful hurricane. . . .

"When this great wind had become charged with the dust of Krakatao, then it stood revealed to human vision. Then it was seen that this wind circled round the earth in the vicinity of the equator, and completed its circuit in about 13 days. The dust manufactured by the supreme convulsion was whirled around the earth in the mighty atmospheric current into which the volcano discharged it. As the dust cloud was swept along by this incomparable hurricane, it showed its presence in the most glorious manner by decking the sun and the moon in hues of un-

136

accustomed splendor and beauty. . . . The progress of the great dust cloud was traced out by the extraordinary sky effects it produced; and from the progress of the dust cloud, we inferred the movements of the invisible air currents which carried it along."

The special feature of the Krakatao eruption was the extreme violence which flung volcanic dust to a height probably never before attained, and produced sea and air waves of an intensity that is hardly equaled in the records of volcanic action. Professor Judd and other geologists think that the suddenness and extreme violence of this eruption was caused by some new crevice or cavity that admitted great volumes of ocean water to the heated strata within the earth's crust; and that these waters were converted explosively into steam which expanded with a force sufficient to blow the mountain into fragments and hurl its debris miles into the air.

A remarkable fact concerning the red sunsets is the great rapidity with which they spread to distant regions of the earth. They appeared around the entire equatorial zone within a few days after the eruption, doubtless because of the great rapidity with which the volcanic dust was carried by the upper air current. Within a week they appeared in every part of the torrid zone—in Australia on September 15, Cape of Good Hope on September 20, and the same day in California and the southern United States.

The rapidity with which the various effects of the Krakatao eruption appeared in all parts of the earth is perhaps the most remarkable outcome of this extraordinary event. The floating pumice, after having made a voyage of nearly 3,750 miles, reached the harbor of St. Paul, a French island in the southern Indian Ocean, on March 22, 1884. Immense quantities of pumice of a similar description, and believed to have come from Krakatao, reached the shores of Madagascar five months later; and no doubt much of it continued for a long time to float around the world.

Another result of the eruption was the series of atmospheric waves caused by the disturbance in the atmosphere which affected the barometer over the entire world. Six days after the explosion, after the atmospheric waves had traveled four times around the globe, the barometer was still affected by them.

Again quoting Sir Robert Ball, "In the late autumn of 1883 the marvelous series of celestial phenomena connected with the great eruption, began to be displayed in Great Britain. The glory of the ordinary sunsets was enhanced by a splendor which has dwelt in the memory of all those who were permitted to see them. There is not the least doubt that it was the dust from Krakatao which produced the beauty of those sunsets, and so long as that dust remained suspended in our atmosphere, so long were strange signs to be seen in the heavenly bodies. But the dust which had been borne with unparalleled violence from the interior of the volcano, the dust which had been shot aloft by the vehemence of the eruption to an altitude of 20 miles, the dust which had thus been whirled round and round our earth for perhaps a dozen times or more in this air current which carried it around in less than a fortnight, was endowed with no power to resist forever the law of gravitation which bids it fall to the earth. It therefore gradually sank downwards. Owing, however, to the great height to which it had been driven, owing to the impetuous nature of the current by which it was hurried along, and owing to the exceedingly minute particles of which it was composed, the act of sinking was greatly protracted. Not until two years after the original explosion, had all the particles with which the air was charged by the great eruption, finally subsided on the earth.

"The Krakatao fine dust reached an altitude of 120,000 feet at first, and was still at a height of 50,000 feet more than a year after the eruption.

"At first there were some who refused to believe that the glory of the sunsets in London could possibly be due to a volcano in the Straits of Sunda, nearly as far away as Australia. But the

138

gorgeous phenomena in England were found to be simultaneous with similar phenomena in other places all around the earth. Once again the comparison of dates and other circumstances proved that Krakatao was the cause of these exceptional and most interesting phenomena.

"Tennyson, ever true to nature, records the event in immortal verse:

" 'Had the fierce ashes of some fiery peak
    Been hurled so high they ranged around the world,
    For day by day through many a blood-red eve
    The wrathful sunset glared.' "

Royal Dutch Airlines

ANAK KRAKATAO, THE ISLAND WHICH ROSE IN JUNE, 1927, SANK IN AUGUST, AND IN FOUR DAYS REAPPEARED WITH ANOTHER ERUPTION. The sea has entered the crater on the left side. From time to time since the great eruption there have been signs

139

of activity below the surface of the sea. In 1927 a submarine volcano reached the surface of the water over a spot where the explosion of 1883 had left water 1,000 feet deep. After disappearing and reappearing, it formed an island called *Anak Krakatao,* which means The Child of Krakatao.

For several years there has been an observation station on Lang Island, set up by the Dutch Government to investigate the activity of Krakatao and warn the inhabitants of the neighboring coasts and islands when an eruption is impending. In January, 1933, rumblings gave warning of another outbreak, and it was possible to predict its approximate date. A photographer was given permission to take photographs of the eruption, and the Dutch Government lent him a boat and an airplane. The ship, carrying the plane, anchored some five miles away and waited. At the moment of eruption, the photographer flew to about fifty yards of the crater's mouth and barely escaped with his life, the wings of his plane being covered with volcanic materials. By this means he was able to obtain the picture shown on page 133.

Tomboro is a volcano on the island of Sumbawa, in the Indian Ocean, east of Java. The eruption of Tomboro in April, 1815, was at that time the most violent eruption of historic times, with the greatest loss of human life—12,000 people. Since then it has been surpassed by Krakatao in 1883, with 36,000 lives lost, and Mt. Pelée in 1902, which destroyed at least 30,000 people.

On April 5, 1815, sounds were heard in several of the neighboring islands which were supposed to be the firing of cannon by pirates. A detachment of troops was embarked on a cruiser and sent in search of the pirates, but they returned on the eighth without having found any occasion for alarm. The eruption began on the fifth, but reached its greatest violence on the eleventh and twelfth. The ashes and dust from the eruption caused darkness which lasted for three consecutive days, at a distance of over three hundred miles; and at noon of April 12 the darkness in Java was so complete that it was impossible to see the hand when held close to the face. The sound of the explosion was heard on the island of Sumatra, 970 miles away, and ash fell to a depth of two feet more than 850 miles distant.

The shooting upward of great columns of matter from the crater produced a violent whirlwind that carried people, horses, cattle, and almost every movable object high into the air, and tore up huge trees by their roots. The eruption was attended by great lava streams that covered vast areas of land and afterward poured into the sea. At the town of Tomboro, an area of land was sunk and remained permanently covered by eighteen feet of water.

In the Province of Tomboro, out of a population of 12,000 only 26 people escaped with their lives.

For the greater protection of the people of these volcanic islands the Netherlands Government has established a volcanological service, through which the symptoms of probable outbreaks may be observed and, by the taking of proper defensive measures, the dangers of volcanic eruptions reduced.

14:

Two Philippine Volcanoes

About six miles from Albay Gulf, *Mayon* rises from a broad plain to a height of about 8,000 feet, forming a perfect cone. Its sides are covered with grass or moss almost to the top. Near the summit are fissures through which steam and sulphurous

MAYON, THE MOST ACTIVE OF THE PHILIPPINE VOLCANOES, IS ALSO CONSIDERED BY MANY TO BE THE MOST BEAUTIFULLY SHAPED VOLCANO IN THE WORLD.

gases escape, and the vapor from these gases which surrounds the summit has a fiery glow at night.

During the nineteenth century there were twenty-six eruptions of Mayon. Perhaps its most destructive eruption in modern times was in 1897 when, on June 23, practically without warning, it began to erupt and continued until June 30. During this time great quantities of lava and ashes were ejected, and streams of lava completely destroyed several villages and severely injured others. The lava flow extended more than seven miles eastward, and a rain of ashes fell as far away as one hundred miles to the east and seventy-five miles to the west. Several hundred lives were lost, mostly from hot blasts and from rolling incandescent materials. In 1914 an eruption of great violence entirely destroyed the town of Cagsaua at the foot of the mountain.

There are said to be fifty recorded volcanoes in the Philippines, of which twelve are active. The most famous of them are Mayon and Taal, both on Luzon Island.

Taal volcano is on an island in Lake Taal, in the southern part of Luzon. On January 30, 1911, there was an explosive eruption from Taal which was the severest volcanic outburst in the Philippines during historic times. The ejected materials were mainly steam, volcanic ash, and mud, with no flow of lava. The mud and ashes spread over an area of 2,000 square kilometers; the crater was deepened; the island subsided, and the surrounding lake changed its level. The clouds of dust and gases went horizontally out and downward along the side of the mountain, as in the case of Mt. Pelée (see page 78). There were 1,335 lives lost, mainly through suffocation from the sulphur dioxide in the escaping steam.

The photograph following shows black mud at the left, still belching from the crater on the day after the explosion.

143

© National Geographic Society—Photograph by Charles Martin

TAAL VOLCANO FROM BAÑADERO THE MORNING AFTER
THE GREAT ERUPTION OF JANUARY 30, 1911.

144

15:

Some Volcanoes of Japan

Japan is an important part of the volcanic belt which encircles the Pacific Ocean. On its various islands there are at least two hundred volcanoes, about fifty of which are more or less active, and eighteen of these smoke all the year round.

Fujiyama rises in solitary majesty 12,395 feet above sea level, about sixty miles southwest of Tokyo. On the south it slopes unbroken to the sea. Its isolation from other mountain ranges and the simple symmetry of its form make it a mountain of remarkable beauty. Fujiyama is richly endowed with legend, and for centuries it has been the commanding motif of Japanese art. The Japanese consider it a sacred mountain, and more than fifty thousand pilgrims climb to its summit every year in midsummer. The ascent is not difficult because of its gentle slope. The crater at the summit is about 2,000 feet in diameter, and is supposed to be from 500 to 600 feet deep.

This is at present a dormant volcano, though several eruptions have occurred within the period of Japan's written history, the last one in 1707. At that time the crater poured forth great streams of lava, and ashes fell to a depth of several inches even in Tokyo. Many consider Fujiyama as now permanently extinct, but experience in other parts of Japan shows that a long quiescent crater may at any time burst into violent and disasterous activity.

145

Three Lions

SNOW-CAPPED FUJIYAMA IS THE MOST FAMOUS
MOUNTAIN OF JAPAN.

146

Three Lions

ASAMAYAMA IN FULL ACTIVITY, AUGUST, 1938.

Asamayama, 8,131 feet high, is one of the best-known and most violently active volcanoes in Japan. In the year 1783 an eruption occurred which at that time was said to be the most frightful eruption on record. Immense rocks were hurled in all directions. One stone, said to be 264 by 120 feet, fell into a river, and it looked like an island. Some forty-eight villages were buried and thousands of lives lost.

Bandai-san, 6,037 feet high, has a terrible interest attached

147

to it. After it had remained quiet so long that the inhabitants of the neighboring districts were lulled into a sense of complete security, suddenly, on July 15, 1888, it burst into fierce activity. Without warning, it discharged a great avalanche of earth and rock which dashed down the sides of the mountain and buried four hamlets, partially destroyed seven villages, killed four hundred sixty-one people, and completely devastated an area of twenty-seven square miles.

Underwood and Underwood

CAULIFLOWER ASH CLOUDS OF VARYING COLOR RISE FROM TWO VENTS OF SAKURAJIMA.

The eruption of *Sakurajima* in 1914 and the scientific studies made in connection with it justify a somewhat detailed account. The following is based on a report made by Dr. T. A. Jaggar, director of the Hawaiian Volcano Observatory, in the *National Geographic Magazine* for April, 1924. From the facts given, it

148

will be seen that the study of this eruption offered the hope that scientists might be able to predict activity in some volcanoes far enough in advance to prevent the loss of many lives.

Sakurajima, 3,506 feet high, is on a small island near the southern extremity of Japan and stands directly opposite the city of Kagoshima in Kagoshima Bay. This city is the capital of the province, with a population at that time of about 70,000 inhabitants. Before the eruption of 1914 there were eighteen villages with about 22,000 people on the shores of this small volcanic island of Sakurajima, which almost fills the bay between Kagoshima and the Osumi promontory. The channel between the city and the volcano was barely two and one-half miles wide.

For a long time scientists had believed that Kagoshima City was in danger from this volcano, and in 1909 and 1910 two writers published warnings that Sakurajima was likely to erupt explosively after violent earthquakes. Experience had taught observers that when "swarms" of earthquakes begin in the vicinity of an active volcano, an eruption will soon follow. During the year 1913 the observatory at Kagoshima had recorded 91 earthquakes, although 34 had been the average over a period of years; and with apprehension the scientists carefully followed the readings of the seismograph.

On the afternoon and evening of January 10, 1914, there were five strong earthquake shocks, and the next morning before sunrise there were three more strong shocks with rumbling noises. On January 11 ten strong shocks were felt and many more were recorded by the observatory seismograph—five shocks an hour during the morning, eleven per hour about noon, and twenty per hour in the evening. Growling noises and roaring as of gas escaping under pressure accompanied most of the earthquakes. In Kagoshima, between six and twelve P.M. on January

149

11, shocks with rumblings were felt about every twenty minutes; from midnight to three A.M. of January 12, every ten minutes, and for the next two hours every five minutes. Between four A.M. on January 11 and ten A.M. of January 12, 417 earthquakes were recorded.

At ten-five on the morning of January 12 the great explosion occurred which relieved the internal strain, and the quakes stopped. Counting the five strong shocks on the afternoon of January 10, there was definite forewarning in noises and earthquake shocks for forty-five hours before the great explosion came.

"These warnings were heeded," writes Dr. Jaggar; "every available sampan sculled with frantic speed back and forth across the channel all day Sunday, January 11th, moving the natives of the island, their bedding, mats, rice bags and canary birds to the mainland. By Monday, the Army, Navy . . . and police officials had taken control; steamship companies, newspaper men and high-school boys organized rescuing expeditions to the island . . . and carried away every living soul they could find. . . . People camped in temple grounds and in cemeteries; business houses offered relief, and 5,000 destitutes were accommodated in schools, temples and public buildings. . . . Probably 95,000 people moved across the country and were cared for by spontaneous hospitality.

"The climax came at 10:05 on Monday morning when, in the middle of the side of the mountain toward Kagoshima, the awe-stricken people saw the hard profile of a swelling balloon of black smoke rise majestically from the ground where an hour before were orange orchards, terraced fields of sugar-cane and gardens of radishes. . . . The jet of smoke shot up obliquely, then straightened to a vertical column, and rose 30,000 feet into the sky, first club-shaped, then assuming the form of a great lily. . . . With occasional lulls, but with ever-increasing violence,

150

the booming concussions of the eruption grew more and more terrible. Flashes of lightning danced through the great billows of smoke and dust, and, in the lower portion of the great black column, vertical lines of upward streaming rocks, bombs, sand and smoke, curling as high as the mountain itself, could be seen from time to time. In addition there were outward spurts of large, glowing blocks which left curling trails of vapor in their path.

"The crisis which resulted in the only loss of life during the disaster occurred at 6:29 P.M. of the same day when a terrible earthquake threw down walls and buildings at Kagoshima, dislodged bowlders from cliffs, and interrupted railway and telegraph service. Fugitives were trapped in land-slides, and a tidal wave with a ten-foot swing caused serious damage to small boats in the harbor. Thirty-five persons were crushed to death and 112 were injured. This quake is to be classed as a 'world shaker' for it was recorded on seismographs in Europe. The lava flows from the volcano had begun, and the gas explosions had relieved the under-earth of millions of tons of matter, so that this quake was probably the evidence of a deep movement, or settling, that had begun along the great chain of Ryu-Ryu volcanoes, extending from Kyushu to Formosa in a string of islets 900 miles to the southwest.

"On January 14th, the worst seemed to be over, and the 15,000 people who had dwelt within the death zone of the volcano, straggled back to the city. Seven out of eighteen villages on the island were destroyed. . . . The falling ashes completely obliterated the village of Hakamagoshi with bombs and gravel. Lava filled the water between the mainland and the island, and converted Sakurajima Island into a peninsula. During a month lava rose to a height of 300 feet above sea level where before there had been water 200 feet deep."

Although this eruption of Sakurajima was the greatest in the annals of Japan, only thirty-five lives were lost by the earthquake

151

in Kagoshima City and elsewhere, and two people jumped into the sea and were drowned; but so far as is known the volcano killed no one, for the scientific prediction of this outbreak enabled the people to flee. In contrast to this, it will be remembered that in Japan's earthquake of 1923, 400,000 lives were lost.

This eruption of Sakurajima is remarkable for (1) the vast amount of material ejected within a brief interval of time; (2) the extraordinary crustal movements within and near the volcano, as shown by the great "swarms" of earthquakes; (3) the close connection of the eruption with a strong tectonic (not volcanic) earthquake; and (4) the removal of all the inhabitants of the island (more than 22,000), which prevented great loss of life.

The eruption was definitely predicted through studies of the premonitory earthquakes; and Dr. Jaggar expressed the hope that in time, through exhaustive studies of volcanic activities, earthquakes may also be predicted with accuracy.

The active volcano *Mihara Yama* stands on the small island of Oshima near Yokohama. The main interest in this volcano lies in the fact that its crater has been a popular place for unhappy Japanese to commit suicide; and during the years of depression, especially, hundreds of people—both men and women—hurled themselves into this crater. In one year alone (1933) there were over two hundred known suicides who believed that Mihara Yama was a sacred place in which they would find eternal rest in the flames of the volcano.

A Tokyo newspaper decided to sponsor a public descent into the crater with the idea of dispelling this superstitious belief, and at the same time to outdo the record of 805 feet into the earth which the seismologist A. Kerner made when he descended into the crater of the Stromboli volcano. A steel "gondola" shaped like a shell and with glass windows was built and attached to a crane that swung out over the crater so it could be lowered and

TOKUZO IWITA RECEIVES CONGRATULATIONS AFTER HIS SECOND DARING DESCENT INTO THE CRATER OF MIHARA YAMA, CALLED "GOD'S FIRE STOVE." The "gondola" is also shown.

153

raised by means of ropes over a pulley. A telephone was installed in the gondola, connected with the surface, and photographic equipment was supplied.

According to an account in the *Illustrated London News,* two members of the staff of the Tokyo newspaper *Yomiuiri Shimbun,* "protected by asbestos suits and wearing gas masks, entered the steel gondola, were swung out by a crane, and were lowered into the abyss. At about 500 feet down, the air seemed to clear and the sides of the crater could be seen, with lava and mud bubbling out of deep fissures. Every five minutes or so, loud explosions broke the deadly silence. Some 700 feet down, the body of a suicide was seen, but attempts to recover it were unsuccessful. Later the remains of numerous other unfortunates were seen, and at one spot, there was the sad spectacle of two little cafe waitresses in their kimonos, lying close together on the same ledge. Reaching 1250 feet, the observers gave the order to pull up the 'gondola.' It was not that the heat was unbearable, but that the force of the eruptions, increasing as the explorers neared the lava bed, made the 'gondola' swing so violently that there was a danger of its being dashed against the crater's walls. The Stromboli record had been broken; though photographs could not be taken below 600 feet." (There are four interesting pictures on page 769 of the *Illustrated London News* of May 19, 1934.)

On Iwo Jima, one of the Volcano Islands, 675 miles south of Tokyo, stands sulphur-smoking *Mt. Suribachi* (554 feet high), upon whose top United States Marines planted the flag on February 23, 1945. The conquest of Japanese-owned Iwo Jima in February and March was an important step up the ladder of island conquests which took American forces to the home islands of Japan itself.

16:

Alaska and the Aleutian Belt

The Aleutian volcanic belt begins on the east at the head of Cook Inlet, in southern Alaska, and extends westward through the Alaskan peninsula and the Aleutian Islands. This is a narrow belt nearly 1,600 miles long. The Aleutian range of mountains is almost wholly volcanic throughout, there being certainly nine and probably twelve or more active or latent volcanoes in the Alaskan continental end of the belt. The Aleutian Islands probably contain a still larger number, and some of the craters constantly send forth steam.

© National Geographic Society—Photograph by R. F. Griggs

KATMAI VOLCANO, 7,500 FEET HIGH, NEAR THE BASE OF THE ALASKAN PENINSULA, ON SHELIKOF STRAIT, IS THE SITE OF ONE OF THE GREATEST ERUPTIONS OF HISTORIC TIMES.

155

On June 6, 1912, without warning, so far as anyone knew, a violent explosion tore off the entire top of *Katmai* Mountain in one of the most tremendous volcanic explosions ever recorded. A mass of ash and pumice whose volume has been estimated at nearly five cubic miles was thrown into the air. This left Katmai as it is shown here, the mere stump of its former self. The white line in the picture indicates approximately the original height of the mountain; and the great arc beneath the line is the rim of the gigantic crater that was left.

The only people who witnessed the explosion from near at hand were two families of native Alaskans who had remained at Katmai after the other people of that town went away to work in a fishing camp.

When the news of Katmai's eruption reached Washington, the National Geographic Society sent geologists to make investigations. According to their reports, the sound of the first mighty explosion had carried down the coast as far as Juneau, 750 miles away, and was even heard across the Alaska Range at Dawson and Fairbanks, 650 and 500 miles away. The column of steam and ash was carried eastward by the wind, and within a few hours had shed a shower of ashes over all the east end of the Alaskan peninsula, the east half of Kodiak Island, and all of Afognak Island. On Kodiak Island, across the strait, the ashes were twelve inches deep. Intense darkness accompanied the fall of ashes, and midnight blackness in the daytime extended as far east as the Kenai peninsula. Darkness lasted for sixty hours at Kodiak, 100 miles from the volcano. Dust fell as far away as Juneau, Ketchikan, and the Yukon valley, 750, 900, and 600 miles away. The fumes were reported from points as remote as Vancouver Island and Puget Sound, 1,500 miles away. Pumice from Katmai formed great floating islands in the water which migrated with the winds and tides and greatly impeded navigators.

Professor R. F. Griggs says of the Katmai eruption: "The magnitude of the eruption can perhaps be best realized if one could imagine a similar outburst in New York City. All of greater New York would be buried under from 10 to 15 feet of ash. Philadelphia would be covered by a foot of gray ash, and would be in total darkness for 60 hours. Washington and Buffalo would receive a quarter of an inch of ash, with a shorter period of darkness. The sound of the explosion would be heard in Atlanta and St. Louis, and the fumes noticed as far away as Denver, San Antonio and Jamaica."

Because of its remoteness from thickly settled vicinities, this gigantic eruption differs from almost all other known great eruptions in that there was practically no damage to property that was used by man and, so far as is known, it was not the direct and sole cause of the loss of a single human life.

There were eruptions of Katmai on a smaller scale in 1914, but the volcano is now quiet. In its crater there now lies a lake of milky-blue water over a mile long and nearly a mile wide, in which is a little crescent-shaped island measuring 400 feet from tip to tip. Explorers who climbed to the top of Katmai have said that the most wonderful of all the sights at the crater was a place where a glacier that was blown in two by the eruption still formed part of the crater wall, the intense heat not being sufficient to melt this palisade of ice. Part of the crater wall is composed of igneous rock of brilliant color.

A few days before the Katmai volcano blew up, early in June, 1912, there was another eruption of great magnitude some miles from Katmai, when great numbers of small volcanoes burst open in the floor of the green valley through which ran the Katmai Trail. There was only one eyewitness to this eruption—the old chief of the Savonoski natives who was on the Katmai Trail when fire seemed to consume the valley. He escaped just in time to avoid destruction.

The explorers believe that this was no reawakening of dormant vents, such as the majority of eruptions are, but that it was

157

the formation of new volcanoes in areas where none had previously existed. These new volcanoes consisted simply of holes blown through the floor of the valley (not of hills or mountains with craters at their tops), and it is thought that soon after their formation they began to throw out enormous quantities of ash and pumice and incandescent material in veritable torrents of fire.

The valley and its branches were found to be covered by a layer of pumice and other volcanic deposits to an unknown depth, and this was covered with ashes from Katmai, showing that these eruptions had taken place before the Katmai explosion and that the latter was only the closing act in the drama.

In September, 1918, Katmai Mountain and the Valley of Ten Thousand Smokes were set aside by proclamation of the president of the United States as the Katmai National Monument. This national park consists of 1,087,990 acres, and includes not only Katmai and the Valley of Ten Thousand Smokes but also several other neighboring volcanoes, such as Novarupta, Mageik, Falling Mountain, Knife Peak, and Martin Volcano, some of which took part in the great upheaval that brought forth such changes in the valley.

"Scientists say that this astounding valley is an example of what the geyser basins of Yellowstone Park were at the time when Yellowstone's volcanoes first ceased their activity; and they predict that in the course of time, probably taking many centuries, the surface here will cool sufficiently for the vents to retain water some distance down. When this happens, the steam below, pressing against the water near the surface, will force this water upward into the air, and a new geyser field will come into existence." (From the National Park Leaflet No. 91973)

158

© National Geographic Society—Photograph by R. F. Griggs

THE VALLEY OF TEN THOUSAND SMOKES, CALLED "THE FIRST WONDER OF THE WORLD," was discovered in 1916 by one of the National Geographic Society's expeditions to the Katmai region. This is the view from the entrance to the great valley seventeen miles long, with its millions of fumeroles always in active operation. Some of the jets throw their steam over a thousand feet into the air, and hundreds of others go up to a distance of five hundred feet, all merging above the valley in one titanic cloud. Around these fumeroles are deposits tinted in all shades of the rainbow, which present a beautiful and awe-inspiring spectacle.

159

NOVARUPTA FROM THE SLOPE OF FALLING MOUNTAIN.
The central lava plug is surrounded by a ring of material that was thrown out in the explosive stage with which this volcano began its existence.

Novarupta volcano is the greatest of all the vents that were newly opened, and appears to be the climax of the activity of the valley. Although newly formed at the time of the big eruption, it is one of the world's largest volcanoes. It burst through the earth not on a mountaintop, but in the bottom of a valley which before the eruption gave no indication of the volcanic forces beneath. Apparently Novarupta began with great explosive violence, for its pumice is scattered over an area ten miles in diameter and more than fifty feet deep in places. After the first violent outburst, the activity gradually diminished in intensity until most of the material was thrown only a short distance, forming a circular crater around the vent. This crater is

160

seven-tenths of a mile in diameter—one of the largest explosive craters in the world—though dwarfed by the vast crater of Katmai.

The only lava bombs found in the Katmai district are those ejected by Novarupta. The explosive activity was followed by the slow extrusion of pasty lava, which has been pushed up in the crater until an immense plug of lava has been formed, 1,200 feet in diameter and extending 250 feet above the floor of the crater. This lava plug is clearly shown in the picture—a steaming mound in the center of the crater. The tremendous quantities of smoke given off continuously, and often filling the sky for miles, show that somewhere beneath this plug the lava is still molten. There are more and larger steaming fissures around Novarupta than anywhere else.

© National Geographic Society—Photograph by J. D. Sayre

KNIFE VOLCANO, WHICH OVERHANGS THE NORTHERN ARM OF THE VALLEY OF TEN THOUSAND SMOKES.

161

Knife volcano is the highest mountain in the Katmai region, overtopping Mageik and all the rest by several hundred feet. It is not at present active, but the snow melts off its flanks sooner than from any other mountains round about. Prior to the National Geographic expeditions this mountain was not known as a volcano, nor had it ever been photographed.

The National Geographic expeditions have brought this great region to the knowledge of the world, and have made discoveries and revelations that have contributed much to the science of volcanology. Through the Valley of Ten Thousand Smokes they made their way back and forth, "plunging through the suffocating vapors, trapping gases for chemical analysis, making soundings, mapping the course of the Valley, and studying the geology of this most amazing example of her processes which Nature has revealed to 20th century man—one of Vulcan's melting pots from which the world is created."

Mt. Wrangell and *Mt. Edgecombe* are two Alaskan volcanoes that are well known. Near the extremity of the peninsula is *Mt. Pavlof,* which has been steaming continually for many years; and farther down the belt is *Mt. Shishaldin,* a beautiful and perfect cone, similar in shape to Japan's famous volcano, Fujiyama.

162

U.S. Navy Official

BEAUTIFUL MT. CAROLI, UNDER ITS HEAVY BLANKET OF SNOW, QUIETLY SMOKES.

This unusual photograph was taken from a United States Navy patrol plane flying high above the clouds over the Alaskan volcanoes, in 1942.

163

Copyright by F. E. Bagger. Courtesy National Geographic Society

An Eruption on Bogoslof Island.

In the Behring Sea, about forty miles west of Unalaska Island, is *Bogoslof Island,* composed entirely of volcanic rock formed by eruptions within historic times. It has been called a "Jack-in-the-box of the sea" because of its many changes of appearance and disappearance.

It was first discovered about 1790 by the Russian admiral Bogoslof, and it was then only one island. During the winter of 1886–87 a new island appeared about two and one-half miles northwest of Bogoslof, and was called New Bogoslof, or Fire

Island. In 1905–06 another peak appeared about halfway between the other islands, and the new one was called Perry Peak. A year later, the officers on a passing ship discovered another peak which absorbed about half of Perry Peak and filled in the space to Castle Rock (as the first island was now called), thus making one island of the group. The new peak was 495 feet high, and they called it McCulloch Peak.

In October, 1907, the same ship returned to the island and found that McCulloch Peak had disappeared. It is thought that the peak exploded on September 1, 1907, as on that date a dense black cloud passed over Unalaska Island, covering the land with ashes which fell about one-half inch thick sixty miles from Bogoslof. In the summer of 1908, officers from a United States revenue cutter found that Perry Peak had also disappeared, and a high ridge of land extended from Fire Island to Castle Rock.

All of these changes were, of course, caused by volcanic action under the surface of the water, piling up masses of lava on different points of the rim of the submarine crater, and causing them to disappear by explosion and collapse of some part of their undersea foundation.

The eruption shown in the picture above will make still further changes in the surface of the island group.

17:

Africa's Great Volcanoes

Mary Light, from *Focus on Africa*, courtesy American Geographical Society of New York

KIBO, THE HIGHEST PEAK OF KILIMANJARO, THE
"GRAND OLD MONARCH OF AFRICA."

Kilimanjaro, the highest known mountain in Africa, is a great extinct volcano of beautiful and majestic proportions, in the territory of Tanganyika, discovered in 1848 by a German missionary, Johannes Rebmann. Its height is not definitely determined, but is about 19,590 feet above sea level. This photograph of the *Kibo* peak was taken from an airplane at 23,000 feet. Notice the wide cloud blankets stretching out beyond, and lower than, the summit.

Another peak of Kilimanjaro is *Mawenzi*, 17,290 feet high.

166

The two peaks are about seven miles apart, and are connected by a saddle which dips down to 14,400 feet. The lava slopes of the Kibo peak are covered to a depth of about 200 feet with an icecap which takes the form of glaciers wherever ravines occur. There are several large glaciers on the sides of Kibo, some of them extending down 400 or 500 feet, and one glacier reaching a lower level of 13,800 feet. Mawenzi is the older core of a former crater, and has no permanent icecap.

Mary Light, from *Focus on Africa*, courtesy American Geographical Society of New York

THIS PHOTOGRAPH IS A CLOSER VIEW OF THE CRATER AND INNER PIT OF KIBO, and shows the icecap which fills the saucer-like crater and sends diverging streams of ice down the sides. The diameter across the crater is about 7,400 feet.

Within sight of Kilimanjaro stands *Mt. Meru*, an old, partly shattered volcano, 14,950 feet in height. Its entire eastern face was blasted away during an eruption.

Some 125 miles west of Kilimanjaro is a pleateau, roughly about 90 by 30 miles, called The Land of the Giant Craters, formed by volcanic materials discharged by a group of some of the largest and most interesting volcanoes in the world. One of the "Giant Craters" is *Ngorongoro*. The greatest diameter of its crater is 13 miles, and its basin is 2,000 feet below the rim. The floor of the crater is nearly level, and contains not only a fresh-water lake fed by streams that flow down the sides of the crater, but also a rich pasture land of red and white clover that feeds great numbers of wild game. At one time it was estimated that 50,000 wild beasts lived here, and 25,000 head of other game including hippopotamuses, rhinoceroses, ostriches, zebras, gazelles, lions, chetahs, hyenas, jackals, baboons, and other animals and numberless birds. The German Kaiser heard of this, and it is said that he planned to establish a meat-canning factory here; but his plan was not carried out, and since then the area has come under game reservation control.

Oldonyo-Lengai, the rose and silver "Mountain of God," is an active volcano that is venerated by the wandering pastoral tribe, the Masai, as the giver of all good things. This volcano sparkles in the sun in flashes, and even from a distance is said to present a picture of enchantment—"one resplendent pyramid of pink, gray and white deposits, arabesqued with folds and furrows of beautiful and varying shapes." The Masai natives explained the internal rumblings that preceded the eruptions of 1917 as the bellowings of cattle that were to come out of the volcano to enrich them.

Mt. Kenya, about 17,040 feet high, has permanent glaciers in the hollows below the summit. *Mt. Elgon*, situated north of Lake Victoria, is an immensely broad and flat volcano, 14,175 feet high. The *Birunga Volcanoes* are not very high, though *Muhavura* rises to 13,550 feet.

West of Lake Victoria, in the Kivu district of the Belgian

168

Congo, is the Albert National Park, and within this park is the *Virunga* (meaning volcano) Range, consisting of eight huge volcanoes that rise from the floor of the Western Rift Valley (which is a branch of the Great Rift Valley, extending from Mozambique up through East Africa and along the Red Sea into northern Syria). The two westernmost volcanoes of the Virunga group are *Tshanina Gongo* and *Nyamlagira,* still very active. In this region a new volcano was formed in 1912 a few miles north of Lake Kivu, and remained active for several weeks while its lava ran down to the lake and nearly filled up a strait between two promontories, practically cutting off a bay of Lake Kivu.

Nyamlagira is a shield volcano, closely resembling those of the Hawaiian type, with very fluid lava which flows out almost like water, spreading out as thin sheets over large areas. Nyamlagira is built up by these sheets of lava piling each one above the previous flow, until it has assumed a form like that of a tortoise shell or shield. Its crater is 10,026 feet above sea level. The lava remains dammed up in pools or lava lakes, as in the Hawaiian volcanoes, and gases rise to the surface of the lava forming great, splashing bubbles that burn with a beautiful yellowish green tinge. Dr. Jean Verhoogen states (in the *National Geographic Magazine* for October, 1939) that "at night the lake becomes a fantastic scene of bright, incandescent lava, which appears to be boiling in the midst of phosphorescent flames." For many years Nyamlagira had displayed activity of this kind, and finally the crater, which is two miles wide, became full of lava which began to spread out over the slopes of the mountain. On January 28, 1938, a number of huge fissures opened on the flanks of the mountain, "a deluge of lava poured out, rushed down at terrific speed, set hundreds of square miles of forest on fire, and trapped large numbers of antelope which were later found completely carbonized. Tremendous founderings occurred in the crater as a result of the drainage of lava through the fissures. The pools collapsed into a deep chimney, and the crater presented a scene worthy of Milton's description of Chaos in *Paradise Lost.*"

At about the same time, an explosion occurred at the foot of the mountain at a place called *Shambene,* and here a new volcano was born. A river of lava issued from the ground and gas vents, cones, and mounds belching lava were scattered in various places over a distance of several hundred yards, with no visible connection between them. The lava from these new vents spread out over the plains for several hundred square miles, destroyed the magnificent forest, and flowed on into Lake Kiva.

18:

Vesuvius

Mount Vesuvius is the best-known volcano in the world, and the only active volcano on the mainland of Europe. It rises in lofty majesty over the Bay of Naples, about seven miles southeast of the city of Naples. Vesuvius stands on the site of an older volcano, Monte Somma, whose ancient ruined crater rim still partly surrounds the cone of the present volcano. The rim of the old cone is seen very clearly in the picture on page 173. From its base, which is thirty miles in circumference, it slopes up to two summits, Monte Somma, the old crater rim, and higher up, within this crater, the new cone of Vesuvius proper. The height of the mountain varies from time to time, but averages 4,000 feet above sea level.

The old volcano seemed to be extinct in the time of the Romans, and they had no traditions of its having been active. During the early years of the Christian Era, an explorer climbed to the summit and reported that its crater was dead and its mouth was choked with vines. The ancients described it as being "a cone-shaped mountain with a flat top, on which was a circular valley filled with vines and grass, and surrounded by high precipices." There were thriving farms and vineyards on its sides, and the cities of Pompeii and Herculaneum flourished at its base near the sea.

In 72 A.D., Spartacus, a rebellious Roman gladiator, encamped in this "vine-covered valley" at the top of the mountain with some thousands of fighting men, and the Roman soldiers were let down the precipices in order to surprise and capture them.

No one was prepared for what occured seven years after the defeat of Spartacus. In the year 79 A.D. a great cloud appeared above Vesuvius, and suddenly the crest exploded, sending forth showers of burning ashes and boiling mud. One side of the "valley" in which Spartacus had encamped—the side toward the sea —was blown off, and its rocks with vast quantities of steam, ashes, burning stones, and sand were thrown far into the sky. The farms and vineyards were wiped out, and the two cities were buried.

We are indebted to the Roman writer Pliny the Younger for the only eyewitness account of the eruption that buried Pompeii and Herculaneum. He was in Misenum, a town eighteen miles from the volcano, and there, with many fugitives from the shaking houses who had gathered together to wait for the light of day, he watched the strange terror before him. His uncle, Pliny the Elder, had gone in a boat earlier in the afternoon to get a closer view of the volcano and to rescue some of his friends who lived at Stabia, across the bay from Misenum. Pliny the Elder was killed at Stabia. Pliny the Younger, in two letters to Tacitus, told of the death of his uncle, and also described what he saw of the volcanic eruption.

He wrote that about one o'clock in the afternoon of August 24, in 79, a new, strange cloud arose from the vine-covered crater of the mountain. It shot up higher and higher, and spread out like a vast pall over the mountain. Earthquakes were violent, the ground rocked, and the waters of the Bay of Naples rose and fell and dashed upon the beaches. Soon the top of the mountain disappeared behind the huge black curtain of smoky steam that was pouring constantly from the crater, and bright flashes of lightning darted through it. There were increasing roars and crashes of terrific explosions deep down under the mountain. As the black cloud spread over the towns around the mountain, the light of afternoon was gradually cut off, and darkness came prematurely. Soon, through this terrifying darkness, bits of pumice stone began falling in showers, and frequently larger blocks of hot lava landed with heavy thuds, just as if they had been thrown

172

Underwood-Stratton

THE INNER CONE OF VESUVIUS AT THE MOMENT OF AN EXPLOSION, AND AN INTREPID AVIATOR.

by the catapults which the Roman armies employed to bombard their enemies with great rocks. The night was one of terror for the inhabitants of Pompeii and the other neighboring towns. Some felt safer in their houses, and stayed there; others felt safer out of doors, for the houses shook continuously.

When daylight came after the night of fear it was exceedingly faint and languid, and night soon apparently returned, for the great black cloud over Vesuvius became still blacker, but was occasionally lit up by angry red flashes. Then a wind that sprang up swept the cloud across to Misenum, and made the darkness so great that it was like the darkness of a room shut up; and through this black darkness, showers of ashes fell constantly.

For eight days and nights this went on, and the enormous quantity of steam sent up, together with the deluge of rain that fell, produced torrents on the mountainside which, carrying onward the falling ashes in streams of mud, overwhelmed everything in their way. Sulphurous vapors filled the air, and violent tremblings of the earth were constant. A city six miles away was quickly made uninhabitable and destroyed by the falling stones. But two others, Herculaneum and Pompeii, which already had suffered from the downpour of ashes, were gradually filled with a flood of water, sand, and ashes which came down the sides of the volcano, covering them entirely.

Strangely enough, there was no flow of lava during this historic eruption of 79 A.D. However, in succeeding eruptions much lava was poured out, and in 472 A.D. another great flood of ashes was added to the covering of the two buried cities.

It was not until about 1700 that the city of Herculaneum was discovered. The peasants of the vicinity had been in the habit of extracting marble from its ruins, and they had also, in the course of years, found many statues. In consequence of this, an excavation was ordered by Charles III, the earliest result being the discovery of the theater and the two famous statues of Hercules and Cleopatra. Many excellent works of art have been unearthed,

BURIED FOR MORE THAN SIXTEEN AND A HALF CENTURIES UNDER A GREAT FLOOD OF ASHES AND MUD FROM VESUVIUS, MANY OF THE RUINS OF POMPEII NOW STAND UNCOVERED.

including the finest examples of mural painting extant from antiquity. The library was also discovered, and over 1,800 papyri were found. Though these had been charred to cinder and were very difficult to unroll and decipher, over three hundred of them have been read.

Herculaneum was buried beneath a flood of volcanic ashes that became cemented by mud, forming a hard crust that sealed up the city. Pompeii, being a few miles farther from the crater, was buried under a deposit of ashes and loose stones, making the

175

work of excavation easier. Although Herculaneum was discovered forty years before the site of Pompeii was found, more rapid progress has been made in bringing Pompeii back to the light of day. A great part of the city has been laid bare—the huge amphitheater and other public buildings. Multitudes of interesting relics have been found, and casts of many of the inhabitants have been obtained by pouring liquid plaster into the ash molds that had remained of them. We see them today in the attitudes and with the expressions of horror with which they met death almost nineteen centuries ago. Many had been holding pillows over their heads, to ward off the blows of the heavier stones which were dropping from the black sky.

The excavations have shown that only a few people did not escape from both cities, and most of them did have ample time to escape. Bulwer-Lytton's account in *The Last Days of Pompeii* which describes the destruction of the city "while all the people were sitting in the theater" is not historically correct.

In 1631 another great explosion took place in which seven streams of lava flowed out of the crater, destroyed several villages on its sides, and took 18,000 lives. Since that time Vesuvius has never been completely quiet, and eruptions have become more and more frequent. In 1906, after a series of threatening earthquakes, the entire top of the cone blew off, and the villages at its base were flooded with molten lava. This eruption lasted for eighteen days, during which time 20,000,000 cubic meters of lava were discharged. Although seven miles away, 100,000 Neapolitans evacuated their city. Steam and dust rose to a height of from six to eight miles. In 1929 another eruption caused great loss of life and property.

176

U.S. Navy Official

THE CITY OF NAPLES OVERTOWERED BY AN ERUPTION OF MT. VESUVIUS IN MARCH, 1944. This eruption added to the Allies' problems in evacuating several thousand inhabitants.

177

Vesuvius and the War

On March 18, 1944, Vesuvius began a week of marked activity, as if to draw attention from the war in Italy, and to show how mild is the bombing fury of man-made wars as compared to Nature's fiery and thunderous upheaval. At four-thirty that afternoon, after several days of warning tremors, molten lava began to pour through fissures in the floor of the crater, flowed over the rim, and rolled down the sides of the mountain. By the afternoon of March 20, the quiet stage seemed to be over, and the explosive stage began. Vesuvius became very violent and hurled into the air great clouds of ashes, hot cinders, and chunks of lava, sending dust and ashes across the entire peninsula. The lava also continued to flow, pushing its way over fields, vineyards, and villages. In an enormous avalanche thirty feet deep and six hundred feet wide, it rolled over the funicular railway that for years had carried tourists up the mountain to peer into the great crater.

Vesuvius stood directly in the path which the Allied armies had to follow from the south on their way to Naples. At the time of this eruption the Allies were already in possession of this region, and press writers were on the ground for the purpose of supplying the newspapers of the Allied Nations with the daily developments of the war. Milton Bracker of the *New York Times* (doubtless pleased to have something besides war news to report) sent by wireless from San Sebastiano, Italy, on March 21, the following account:

"At 12:30 o'clock this morning a giant tongue of lava from Vesuvius crashed into the stone house where Giuseppe Battaglio has lived for years with his wife, Maria, and their six children. By one o'clock the house had been pulverized and buried under the countless tons of molten stone. The stream of lava continued inexorably on its way toward the main street of this town which

British Official

No Thoroughfare!

The lava moves relentlessly up the main street of San Sebastiano. Beneath this rough mass lies the molten lava, and every few minutes its forward movement forces the huge pile of rocks and rubble aside, and the molten lava streams forth and gains a few more yards in its destructive journey.

179

has 2,500 inhabitants, and nestles on the volcano's northwest slope, eight miles from Naples.

"Early yesterday afternoon, on orders of the Allied Military Government, San Sebastiano's inhabitants and those of the near-by Massa di Somma began their pitiful evacuation, which was in full swing late last night when the liquid avalanche, hotter than boiling, cascaded down the valley. This correspondent stood within 50 feet of the lava stream when it demolished the first house in town. . . . Another spectator was Lieut. Col. Charles Poletti, military governor of the Naples area. With his staff he directed the civilian evacuation in army trucks, and announced that the Allies were prepared to feed the refugees tomorrow. Some were taken to Naples, others to Santa Anastasia and others possibly to Aversa. The larger town of Cercola was next in line, should the lava continue to flow after having inundated this doomed community.

"Those who watched Vesuvius in action this morning will never forget it. The crater, from which alternately oozed or spurted the fiery volcanic matter, was forgotten in the presence of one prong of lava 100 yards wide and actually 30 feet deep. It was like the monstrous paw of an even more monstrous lion, slowly inching forward toward his prey.

"The lava was white-hot; it was orange-gold, with occasional black patches, undulating like waves. As the stream advanced, great bowlders cracked off and tumbled down, setting fire to small fruit trees and causing onlookers to leap back in alarm. The general sound was like that of an infinite number of clinkers rolling out of a furnace, but sometimes a great chunk of rock bent rather than broke. Its effect was like that of the devil's own taffy being pulled and twisted to suit his taste.

"The rate of flow earlier had been officially estimated at 12 feet a minute. Last night and this morning the lava acted capriciously: here and there it leaped ahead with searing tentacles, and at other times it seemed to slow up, as if gathering weight to

180

NIGHT PHOTOGRAPH OF VESUVIUS IN ERUPTION SHOWING RED-HOT LAVA STREAMING DOWN THE MOUNTAIN ON MARCH 22. A terrific electrical storm hovered around the crater, and each time the volcano threw up molten lava, forked lightning stabbed the skies, adding to a never-to-be-forgotten scene for Allied troops in the area.

181

overwhelm a ridge in the valley.

"At one side stood a peasant whose weathered face turned tawny in the glow. 'Guerra, fame, distruzione,' (war, hunger, destruction) he repeated, shaking his head. 'Guerra, fame, distruzione!'

"But there was humor, too. An American corporal from Indiana squatted at a safe distance and muttered: 'Gosh, when I tell 'em about this in Muncie!'

"Gradually the stream spread out in the valley. The last few trees went up in flames, and then the crackling mass crunched down on an eight-foot wall and began to devour it. Giuseppe Battaglio's house was on the far side of the wall, and for a while it seemed that it might channel the flow and save the modest stone dwelling. But as the incandescent mass roared over the wall, it was plain that the house was fated. A spear of fire shot up to a corner of the building; then it subsided, and the house seemed to be winning the battle. The odds were too great, however. The lava ground into the base on the other side, and with a roar, the wall fell in. A few minutes later the surging flow literally cracked the house in half. What looked like an iron bedstead twisted into the air.

"Thus the destruction of the town began. A few hundred yards back, but directly in line of the flow, stood the town's best houses, and the three-story yellow school that the inhabitants cherished. It was estimated that they were all crushed and buried within two hours."

A reporter for the Associated Press adds: "The Allied soldiers in San Sebastiano already had cleared out all the residents who would go. Some, mostly old and sick people, had refused to leave, cowering in their homes. Once it became certain that the houses were in the path of the stream, the soldiers were told to remove everyone, regardless of their desires. They smashed open doors with their rifle butts, and went through the houses room by room for anyone left behind. As they went through, fumes from the

182

British Official

SAN SEBASTIANO'S CHERISHED SCHOOLHOUSE IS GRADUALLY
OBLITERATED BY THE HOT, CRUNCHING STREAM OF AA LAVA.

approaching lava were already filling the rooms.

"Lava poured over a gasoline dump and there was an explo-

183

sion—big as explosions go, but trifling compared with what was happening inside Vesuvius. Then the lava poured over a well, sealing it, and at the same time bringing its water to the boiling point. The well exploded in a geyser, breaking through the crust of lava that had just covered it."

One man who refused to be evacuated from the tortured slope of the mountain was Professor Giuseppe Imbo, director of the Vesuvius Royal Observatory, and one of the foremost authorities on volcanoes. During the four most exciting days of the eruption, Professor Imbo either remained in his observatory watching the eruption, checking his seismograph, and making records, or else climbed about the mountainside to test the temperature of the lava or measure the rate of its flow. When the lava flow slackened, he journeyed, on foot, four miles down the mountain to tell the Allied officials that evacuations were no longer necessary.

Acme Photo

AMERICAN PLANES WERE CAUGHT IN THE DELUGE
OF ASHES FROM VESUVIUS.

A 12th A.A.F. airdrome was located at the base of the mountain,
and was caught in the deluge of molten lava flowing down the
mountainside. Although the volcanic eruption brought extensive
destruction to the airdrome, crews went to work immediately to
repair it, and soon the bombers were winging out in raids over
enemy territory as usual.

185

19:

Three Mediterranean Volcanoes

Stromboli is a famous volcano rising abruptly out of the sea on one of the Lipari Islands north of Sicily. As far back as records carry us it has emitted fire and smoke, and is one of the most active volcanoes in the world. Stromboli was mentioned by several writers as being active before the Christian Era, but commencement of its activity extends into the past beyond the limits of tradition. Since history began, its action has never wholly ceased, and it is almost the only volcano, if not the only one, that is never entirely quiet, although it may have varied in intensity from time to time. Its action is always most intense when the barometer is lowest.

For centuries this remarkable volcano has been called "The Lighthouse of the Mediterranean." Since it can be seen one hundred miles out to sea, its regular flashes are relied upon by seamen.

Its principal crater is about two-thirds of the way up the mountain, and there are several small craters on one side. Because of the position of the main crater, it is possible to ascend the mountain and look down upon the crater from above. While there are small explosions going on continually, the more violent eruptions are from seven to fifteen minutes apart. Several eminent observers, by accurate measurement of the minutes, have approached quite near the crater. One geologist, his legs held by companions, stretched his head over the precipice. He looked straight down into the mouth of one of the vents of the crater immediately under him, and watched the play of liquid lava within it. "Its surface resembled molten silver, and was con-

Underwood-Stratton

STROMBOLI, "THE LIGHTHOUSE OF THE MEDITERRANEAN" BY
NIGHT, SENDS FROM ITS CRATER "A PILLAR OF CLOUD BY
DAY," WITH ASHES FALLING IN SHOWERS FROM THE
EDGE OF THE CLOUD. (August, 1912.)

187

stantly rising and falling at regular intervals. A bubble of white vapor rose and escaped, with a decrepitating noise, at each ascent of the lava—tossing up red-hot fragments of scoria which continued dancing up and down with a sort of rhythmic play upon the surface."

At intervals of fifteen minutes or more, there was a pause in these movements within the crater. A loud report then followed, the ground trembled, and an immense bubble of vapor rose to the surface of the lava. This bubble burst with a crackling noise, and threw out to the height of about 1,200 feet large quantities of red-hot stones and scoria which fell in a fiery shower all around. Another brief rest, and the more moderate action was resumed as before.

The crater of Stromboli seems always to be choked by a partial floor of semisolid lava. This may be caused by the fact that its crater is open at the side, and allows cool air to get in freely and harden the lava rapidly. It has been thought that in the intervals between "flashes," the gas bubbles from the liquid lava in the chimney gradually accumulate and gather under the partial floor of the crater. Soon the smaller bubbles join to form a big one, and by that time the pressure is strong enough to cause an explosion. The floor is blown upward, and the "lighthouse" flashes red upon the steam cloud which always hangs above the peak. This process has gone on regularly for hundreds of years. If Stromboli should have a great explosion which breaks up this mild and regular action in the crater floor, it would probably wreck its useful lighthouse mechanism and convert it into a commonplace volcano instead of a unique beacon.

Not many years ago a seismologist, A. Kerner, made a descent into one of the craters of Stromboli, so it is said, to a depth of 805 feet. This held the record for volcanic adventure until a descent of 1,250 feet was made into a Japanese volcano. (See pp. 153–154.)

An Old Drawing of Mt. Etna in Eruption.

On the eastern shore of Sicily, in the Mediterranean Sea, is the largest and highest of European volcanoes—*Mt. Etna*—more than 10,870 feet above sea level. The base of the mountain is eighty-seven miles in circumference, with lava completely surrounding it to a wide extent. Its summit is usually covered with snow. Etna is so high that the recent eruptions have rarely been of sufficient energy to throw the lava quite up to the crater at the summit. As a consequence, there are numerous subsidiary or "parasite" craters and cones all around the flanks of the mountain, so that it has become a cluster of volcanoes rather than a single volcanic cone. There are about two hundred of these subsidiary cones, some of them over 3,000 feet high. The remarkable stability of the mountain appears to be due to the innumerable dikes which penetrate the lava flows and tuff beds in all directions, and thus bind the whole mass together.

From the earliest times, Mt. Etna has been the subject of leg-

189

ends. The Greeks believed it to be either the mountain with which Zeus had crushed the giant Typhon, or the workshop of Hephaestus and the Cyclops. Its eruptions have been numerous, records of them extending back to several centuries B.C., and unrecorded ones doubtless took place much further back. Thucydides mentions eruptions in the eighth and fifth centuries B.C.

After the breaking out of Vesuvius in 79 A.D., Mt. Etna enjoyed longer periods of repose. However, its eruptions since that time have been numerous, especially during intervals when Vesuvius was quiet, there being a sort of alternation between periods of great activity of the two volcanoes. There are also not a few instances of both of them having been in action at the same time.

Thousands of lives and many towns have been destroyed by the numerous outbursts of Mt. Etna. In the eruptions of 1169, about 15,000 people were buried in the ruins of Catania; and in 1669, 20,000 people perished. The most spectacular eruption known in its history was in 1853.

In November, 1928, grave consternation was caused by a sudden renewed activity of Etna. The Messina–Catania railway line was blocked by streams of lava 100 feet wide, descending from the crater at an average speed of 20 feet a minute, and all land communication between Catania and Messina was cut off. On November 7 the lava reached the sea. The town of Mascati was completely wiped out, and the village of Nunziata almost entirely destroyed.

In spite of the destruction wrought by Mt. Etna, the Sicilians still cling to the fertile slopes of this deadly mountain, and refuse to give up their farms and vineyards. The volcanic soil around this mountain is said to rank with the richest on earth, sometimes yielding five crops a year.

190

Underwood-Stratton

Etna Again Spreads Destruction over a Wide Area.
The Boiling Lava Is Fast Approaching Catania.

191

VULCANO AS SEEN FROM THE SUMMIT OF VULCANELLO.

The most southern of the Lipari Islands in the Mediterranean Sea is *Vulcano,* the home of a volcano that was very important in Roman mythology. (See p. 21.) Active long before the Christian Era, it still emits sulphurous and other vapors.

The type of eruptions from Vulcano has set the pattern for one of the four kinds of volcanic explosiveness: the Hawaiian type, the Peléean type (see p. 85), the Strombolian type, and the Vulcanian type. Professor Lacroix describes the Vulcanian type of eruption as:

"Magma very viscous; between explosions, completely solidified at the surface; each explosion therefore tears with it many sharp fragments of the crust. As a result, the eruption clouds are very dense, gray to black, appearing dark even by night. The lapilli are angular, the bombs bread-crusted; pumiceous within and glassy at the periphery."

Vulcano's main office at the present time, however, is to serve as a sulphur mine. Thus the peak which gave title to all fire-breathing mountains has become a servant to man.

192

20:

The Island of Fire and Ice

THE LARGEST CRATER OF MT. HEKLA, ICELAND'S
BEST-KNOWN VOLCANO.

Old superstition called *Mt. Hekla* "the back gate to hell." It was active until less than one hundred years ago, and may become active again. Hekla has had twenty severe eruptions within historic times, covering the surrounding country with lava and ashes, and terrible destruction has followed in their wake. One of its eruptions continued for six years without stopping. Hekla's eruption of 1845 is one of the greatest eruptions in the history of Iceland.

193

In the period since 1500 A.D., Iceland has exceeded all other places in the outflow of lava, having poured out upon this small island one-third of the world's entire output of lava, according to Dr. Sapper's estimate. In regard to the violence of their eruptions, and to the number of volcanoes concentrated in a small space, Iceland is one of the most volcanic countries in the world. There are 107 volcanic mountains known to exist on the island, and no less than 20 of these have been active during historical times. Hekla in the south and Scaptar in the north are the best known.

The whole of Iceland is due to the work of subterranean forces, being entirely made up of volcanic rocks, and it has seemingly been built up during the ages from the depth of the sea. The tablelands of Iceland are composed mainly of lava poured out ages ago from fissures in the earth's crust, but many of the volcanic rocks which form so great a part of its area are recent lavas from its active volcanoes.

The higher portions of the island are covered by large ice fields similar to the icecap under which Greenland lies buried. The largest of these ice fields is the Vatna Jökull, three times the size of Rhode Island. In some places an active volcano projects above the icecap. When an eruption takes place under these circumstances, the result is terrible indeed. The red-hot lava, rushing from the crater and falling on the ice, causes it to melt suddenly, and a torrent of steaming water, mud, rocks, and pieces of ice comes roaring down the slopes into the valley below. The eruptions are often accompanied by dreadful floods. Nowhere else in the world are the two extremes of fire and ice so intimately associated as in Iceland; and nowhere is the meeting of these two extremes attended with so much disaster.

Although Hekla is Iceland's best-known volcano, especially after its great eruption of 1845, there are also others which deserve attention. One of the most interesting of these is *Askja,* an immense crater in the east-central section of the island. Even in Iceland, Askja was relatively unknown until 1875, when a tremendous eruption occurred. On the north, west, and south of Askja lies a large lava field called the *Odadahraun* or Evil-Deed Lava, so named because this lava from Askja wrought such havoc in the valleys and plains which it penetrated. It is impossible to describe the utter desolation, the terrible tangle of stiffened lava billows, the crumpled ridges and blister caves that extend for miles in all directions from Askja.

One of Iceland's loftiest mountains is *Oeraefa Jökull.* In 1362 a flood of melted snow and ice from this volcano swept forty farms, together with their inhabitants and livestock, bodily into the ocean.

The eruption of *Skaptar Jökull* in 1783 is one of the most remarkable of historic eruptions in Iceland, and up to that time it was the greatest volcanic eruption known in history. It is still classed with only two or three others of later date as being one of the most terrible of all volcanic disasters. It was on June 8, 1783, that Skaptar Jökull, after a series of earthquakes, became exceedingly violent and began emitting volcanic vapors. On the eleventh, immense torrents of lava began to be poured forth from numerous mouths along a fissure nearly fifteen miles long—a marvelous example of a fissure eruption.

The account of the journey made by these lavas reminds one of some of the fabulous folk legends of the Norse giants: These torrents of lava from the different openings united to form a stream which, flowing down into the river Skapta, not only dried it up, but completely filled the vast gorge through which the river had held its course. This gorge was 200 feet wide and from 400 to 600 feet deep, and the lava filled it so entirely that it overflowed to a considerable extent the fields on either side. After leaving this ravine full and overflowing, the lava pushed on into a deep lake which lay in the course of the river. Here its progress was arrested for a while until it ultimately filled the bed of the

195

lake altogether, either drying up its waters or chasing them before it into the lower part of the river's course. The molten lava, still pouring from the mountain, forced the hot stream onward, and it continued its advance until it reached some volcanic rocks which were full of caverns. Into these caverns the lava entered, and where it could not eat its way by melting the old rock it forced a passage by shivering the solid mass and throwing its broken fragments into the air to a height of 150 feet.

On June 18 there appeared above the first mouth another one of large dimensions. From this opening poured another immense torrent of lava which flowed very rapidly over the solidified surface of the first stream, and ultimately combined with the part that was still flowing to make a more formidable main current. When this fresh stream reached the fiery lake which had filled a lower portion of the valley of the Skapta, a part of it was forced up the channel of that river toward the foot of the hill where the river has its source. After pursuing its course for several days, the main body of this lava stream reached the edge of a great waterfall called Stapafoss, which plunged into a deep abyss. Pushing the water out of its way, the lava here leaped over the precipice and formed a great cataract of fire. After this, it filled the channels of the river, extending itself far beyond it in breadth, and followed it until it reached the sea.

The third day brought fresh supplies to the flood of lava still pouring from the mountain. There being no room in the channel, now filled by the former lurid stream which had pushed up toward the northwest, the fresh lava was forced to take a new direction toward the southeast where it entered the bed of another river. Here it pursued a course similar to that which flowed through the channel of the Skapta, filling up the deep gorges and then spreading itself out into great fiery lakes over the plains.

The eruption of lava from the mountain continued for two years, with some short intervals, and so enormous was the quantity of lava poured forth during this period that, according to a careful estimate which has been made, the whole together would form a mass equal to that of Mt. Blanc. One of the streams was fifty and the other forty miles in length. The Skapta branch of the flow sustained a breadth varying from twelve to fifteen miles on the plains; that of the other was only about half as much. Each of the currents has an average depth of one hundred feet, but in the deep gorges it is no less than six hundred feet in depth. Eleven years later vapor continued to rise from these great streams, and the water contained in the numerous fissures of the lava was hot.

Partly owing to the sudden melting of the snows and glaciers of the mountain, partly to the stoppage of the river courses, immense floods of water deluged the country in the neighborhood, destroying many villages and a large amount of agricultural and other property. Twenty villages were overwhelmed by the lava currents.

This was a national disaster for Iceland. One-fifth of its inhabitants (10,000), four-fifths of its sheep (190,480), three-fourths of its horses (28,000), and more than half of its cattle (11,460) were destroyed. This dreadful destruction of life came about partly by the direct action of the lava currents, partly by the poisonous vapors they emitted, partly by the floods of water, partly by the destruction of the herbage by falling ash, and lastly, as a consequence of the desertion of the coasts by the fish, which formed a large portion of the food of the people.

The immense flows of lava from Skaptar-Jökull exceeds in volume any other flow known during historic times. In addition to this, ashes covered the entire island and the surface of the sea for miles around its shores. The atmosphere over Iceland was loaded with fine dust for months; crops were destroyed in Scotland, 600 miles away; plants were blighted and sulphurous fumes were noted even in Holland, 1,000 or 1,200 miles away. On several occasions the ashes were drifted by the winds over considerable parts of the European continent, obscuring the sun and giving the sky a gray and gloomy aspect. In certain respects, they produced the same kind of phenomena in the heavens that were produced by the explosion of Krakatao, which occurred just a century later, in 1883.

Throughout Iceland glaciers and volcanoes exist side by side. Many slumbering volcanoes carry enormous glaciers upon their tops and sides. The glaciers of Iceland have a combined area of some 5,300 square miles, more than three times the area of the glaciers of the Alps. This island, like Yellowstone Park, is famous for its geysers and hot springs. Clouds of white steam are seen in almost every valley.

21:

Volcanoes of the United States

Lassen Peak stands 10,453 feet above sea level in the western half of the Lassen Volcanic National Park, in northeastern California. This park, consisting of nearly 164 square miles, was established by Congress in 1916 to preserve the peak and other volcanic features contained in this area.

The first known eruption of Lassen Peak since the coming of the white man was on May 30, 1914, when a puff of steam from the summit attracted the attention of the whole region. On the next day a member of the Forest Service reported that a hole twenty-five by forty feet in size had been opened in the snow within the old crater at the top of the mountain, and that rock fragments and dust were scattered over the snow around the pit to a distance of three hundred feet. Other eruptions followed, and in the towns of the Upper Sacramento Valley a special ring of the fire bell was decided upon to call out the people to see the eruptions.

During the first year there were more than 150 eruptions, and some of them were sufficiently violent to hurl a column of smoke to a height of ten thousand feet. A few stones were thrown as far as a mile from the crater.

On May 19, 1915, the first glowing lava made its appearance, rising in the new crater and spilling through a notch in the crater's rim in the form of a tongue which reached one thousand feet down the slope. During the night of May 19 the snow was melted on the northeastern slope, causing destructive flows of mud which swept twenty-ton boulders five to six miles into the valleys of Hat Creek and Lost Creek.

Three days later, on May 22, another and lesser mud flow

199

moved down the same slope, and minor flows took place on the north and west flanks of the mountain. At the same time a terrific hot blast, heavily charged with dust and rock fragments, was discharged down the northeast flank of the peak. So violent was the outburst that trees on the slopes of Raker Peak, more than three miles away, were felled uniformly in the direction of the onrushing blast. At the same time a vertical column of smoke and ash rose more than five miles above Lassen's crater.

The energy of the volcano was largely spent by the end of the 1915 eruptions, but a series of explosions occurred in May and June, 1917. The activity after 1915 produced little effect besides modifying the form of the crater by opening new vents within it. Most of the crater is now filled by the rough, blocky lava which rose into it in May, 1915.

It is thought that the eruptions of 1914 were stimulated by water from melting snow seeping down through cracks in the mountainside until it reached the still liquid magma which was already slowly solidifying in the dome, and started the steam explosions.

As it stands today, the mountain has passed through two stages of growth. The earlier Lassen was a broad, gently sloping volcano of the shield type, built of layer upon layer of lava. It rose by a succession of lava flows to an elevation above 8,500 feet, with a base five miles across from north to south, and seven miles from east to west. In the second stage, the steep Lassen cone was built on this broad, substantial platform. This, the more conspicuous portion, represents a still rarer dome type of volcano, formed by stiff, viscous lava which was pushed up through the vent, like thick paste squeezed from a tube. Piling up, in and around the old crater, this stiff lava rose in a bulging, domelike form high above it.

Henry Lind, National Park Service

LASSEN PEAK, THE ONLY RECENTLY ACTIVE VOLCANO IN THE
U. S. MAINLAND, WITH MANZANITA LAKE IN THE FOREGROUND.

201

National Park Service

THE CRATER OF CINDER CONE, TEN MILES FROM LASSEN PEAK. One of the most interesting features of the Lassen Volcanic National Park is *Cinder Cone* with its many-colored dunes and its rugged lava beds. There were lava flows from Cinder Cone in 1850, which occurred during the first volcanic eruption observed by white men in the United States proper. The present cone had been piled up much earlier than this by explosive cinder eruptions, and lava flowed out from its base. Then followed a second series of cinder eruptions, and also a second series of lava flows. The last lava flow was in 1851, when flaring lights were observed from various distant points for many nights.

Mt. Diller and *Pilot Pinnacle,* along with *Black Butte* and *Brokeoff Mountain,* are remnants of one great caldera that was left when the upper part of a large mountain (now known as *Mt. Tehama*) was destroyed in some long-ago explosion and possible collapse. This mountain once stood three miles southwest of Lassen Peak, with a base more than twelve miles in diameter, and rose approximately 4,000 feet above the boiling springs of Sulphur Works. It was formed by a succession of quiet lava flows

202

MT. DILLER AND PILOT PINNACLE, WITH A STEAMING VENT
OF SULPHUR WORKS, AND A SKI SLOPE IN THE FOREGROUND.

alternating with explosive eruptions. The many fumeroles and
hot springs in the old caldera show that the lava beneath the
surface has not yet entirely cooled.

Mt. Shasta, 14,350 feet high, is another one of California's
volcanic peaks. Its summit is 400 feet above the timber line, and
is occupied by small glaciers. On the west side, 2,000 feet below
the summit, is a cone with a crater at its top known as *Shastina.*
On the lower slopes and in surrounding regions are a number of
small craters, some built of cinders and others of lava. Mt. Shasta
is a typical strato-volcano, composed mainly of lava flows, and
on its flanks are well-defined lava streams. In one of these lava
streams on the lower slope of the mountain, the surface of the
lava cooled and hardened while the central part of the stream
flowed out, leaving an enormous opening from 60 to 80 feet high,
20 to 70 feet broad, and at least a mile long, with a lava roof
from 10 to 70 feet thick. It is called Pluto's Cave.

U.S. Geological Survey

LAVA FLOWS OF THE COLUMBIA PLATEAU, EXPOSED BY EROSION OF THE COLUMBIA RIVER, AT BIGGS, OREGON.

The *Columbia Plateau* is an immense lava field extending through Washington, Oregon, and far into Idaho, and merging with the Cascade Mountains. It joins the Snake River Plain which reaches western Wyoming. The Columbia Plateau has an area of from 200,000 to 250,000 square miles. It is not one vast flow, but is composed of many independent sheets which overlap and supplement one another (as may be seen in the picture), so as to form a continuous and highly compound system. This lava field is 4,000 feet thick in some places, as can be seen in the walls of the canyons cut in the lava by the Columbia and Snake Rivers. Some of this lava may have come from great volcanic peaks like Shasta and Rainier, and many craters are still left on the plateau; but most of it probably came through fissures in a highly fluid condition, and spread over the country without forming volcanic mountains. The surface of the Columbia lava is covered with deep, rich soil which has resulted from the slow disintegration and decay of the basalt, and furnishes the rich wheat lands for which Oregon and Washington are so famous.

Bureau of Reclamation

THE COLUMBIA LAVA FLOWS OF LONG AGO MADE POSSIBLE
THIS GREAT RESERVOIR OF WATER BEHIND THE GRAND
COULEE DAM WHICH SPANS THE COLUMBIA RIVER
IN THE STATE OF WASHINGTON.

The *Grand Coulee* is a deep canyon cut by erosion in the Columbia lava, a trench with vertical walls from 300 to 400 feet high, between which there is a flat-bottomed valley from one and a half to four miles broad. The length of its main part is about thirty miles. This canyon is caused by a break, or fault, in the lava, and enlargement of this break by river erosion.

In recent years the United States Government has utilized this great trench in the lava by building a massive dam across it (shown in the picture), making an enormous reservoir for the water supply of the surrounding country. The Grand Coulee Dam

205

is the largest man-made structure in the world—three times the size of the largest pyramid in Egypt—and is probably the greatest engineering feat so far accomplished by man. The storage reservoir behind the dam is 151 miles long and extends to the Canadian border. The purposes of this dam are flood control, irrigation of vast areas of farmlands that would otherwise be barren, and the development of power to be used over large sections of the Northwest.

Crater Lake National Park

CRATER LAKE AND WIZARD ISLAND.
The waters of *Crater Lake* occupy the site of what was once Mt. Mazama, a large volcano in Oregon. This beautiful lake, 6,239 feet above sea level, is more than 2,000 feet deep. It is six miles long and four miles wide, and is encircled by cliffs from 500 to 2,000 feet high, making this vast cauldron about

4,000 feet deep in places. At some time in the past, a great explosion caused so much material to be thrown out from the magma chamber beneath the volcano that the entire top of the mountain collapsed, leaving a great caldera. Williams estimates that "approximately one-tenth of Mt. Mazama was blown away in fragments, and that the remaining nine-tenths collapsed into the underlying reservoir when it was suddenly drained." After this explosion and collapse, more lava came up through the floor of the cauldron, forming a perfect volcanic cone. This cone is now Wizard's Island, as shown in the picture.

The ancient site of Mt. Mazama with its Crater Lake has been set aside as a national park.

Stretching southwest from Tycho Crater is one of the most remarkable lava flows in the world. Because of its rich, shining blue color, and because its branching folds of pahoehoe suggest the claws and legs of some fantastic, dragon-like monster, it has been called The Blue Dragon Lava Flow. This amazing region of folds, whirlpools, gigantic snakes, and frozen waves extends for about eleven miles.

The lava fields of southern Idaho are from the most recent fissure eruptions in the United States—probably not many hundreds of years ago. There were not only quiet lava flows in this section, but also explosive eruptions that built up cinder cones, spatter cones, lava cones, and craters in great profusion. There are also canyons, caverns, pahoehoe and other lava flows, great mounds and chimneys, volcanic tufa—perhaps more volcanic features than are to be found in such a small area anywhere else in the United States. Because these craters and cones have the appearance of the surface of the moon when seen through a telescope, this section is called The Craters of the Moon. The highest crater is Big Cinder Butte, about 600 feet high, and is one of the largest basaltic cinder cones in the world.

207

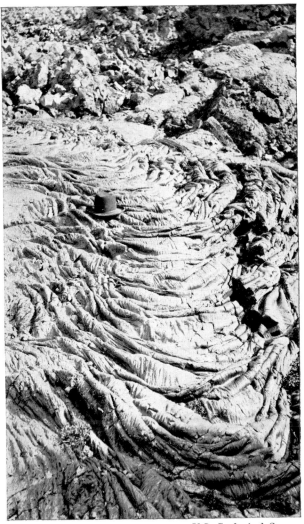

U.S. Geological Survey

THE BLUE DRAGON LAVA FLOW IN THE CRATERS OF THE MOON NATIONAL MONUMENT NEAR ARCO, IDAHO.

One of the most interesting volcanic regions of the United States is the *Craters of the Moon*, a section of about eighty square miles set aside as a national park for the preservation of its volcanic features.

208

J. R. Eyerman, from Washington State Progress Commission

MT. RAINIER, IN THE STATE OF WASHINGTON, IS ONE OF AMERICA'S MOST BEAUTIFUL EXTINCT VOLCANOES.

209

Mt. Rainier is 14,325 feet high, rising practically from sea level in plain view from many sections. Its summit is covered with snow and beautiful glaciers, several of which may be seen in the above photograph.

In the Cascade Mountains, through Washington and Oregon, there are many other picturesque extinct volcanoes. The best-known of these are Mt. Hood, Mt. Baker, Mt. Jefferson, and Mt. St. Helens.

Of the hundreds of lava flows and craters within the United States, all except the most ancient ones are confined to the western part of the country, which comprises a part of the great volcanic belt surrounding the Pacific Ocean. Not only are Washington, Oregon, Idaho, and California rich in volcanic features, but Utah, Colorado, Nevada, New Mexico, and Arizona also have interesting remains of volcanism.

About 125 miles south of Salt Lake City are several interesting craters known as the *Ice Spring Craters.* Three of these craters of scoria and lapilli are nearly perfect in form, but the lava eruptions followed by explosions broke the crust of the craters in some places. Lava flows from the Ice Spring Craters cover an area of about twelve and one-half square miles, and probably average fifty feet deep.

A few miles south of Ice Spring Craters there is another more recently extinct volcano called *Tabernacle Crater,* because of its resemblance, when seen at a distance, to the Salt Lake City Tabernacle.

There are a number of basaltic cones in Colorado; but Colorado's most interesting examples of the ruins of ancient volcanoes are the *Spanish Peaks* in the southeastern part of the state, about sixty miles south of Pueblo. There are two sharp, conical peaks, 12,720 and 13,620 feet above sea level, from which radiate a number of wall-like ridges formed by dikes which mark the course of fissures.

U.S. Geological Survey

THE BODKIN, A VOLCANIC NECK NEAR THE BASE OF THE MT. TAYLOR MESA, NEW MEXICO.

211

Ages ago, a large section of western New Mexico was covered with lava flows which made a layer of lava about three hundred feet deep. The rocks and soil outside this lava field were gradually worn down by erosion, and this left a high tableland, or *mesa,* about forty-seven miles long and twenty-three miles wide, high above the surrounding country. This tableland had a strong, heavy cap of lava which protected it from the rapid erosion by rivers, rains, and winds which lowered the surrounding plains. When the volcanoes on this mesa stopped erupting, the lava slowly cooled and solidified in the chimneys through which it came, and plugs of dense rock were formed. Some of these "necks" of volcanic rock in the ancient chimneys remained as prominent landmarks after the general surface was lowered by erosion. Two other volcanic necks in New Mexico are shown on page 48.

Rising upon this tableland is a volcanic pile named *Mt. Taylor,* composed almost entirely of lava, which gives its name to the mesa. There are also scores of cinder cones still to be seen on the Mt. Taylor Mesa.

In northern Arizona are the *San Francisco Mountains* of volcanic origin, and adjoining them are many smaller peaks with perfectly formed craters of black basalt. Nearly four hundred cinder cones, spatter cones, craters, and vents are to be found in this area, and many occur in other parts of Arizona as well.

The section of the United States that lies in the Pacific-coast volcanic belt is the only part of our country where volcanic action is likely to take place. However, with America's organized Forest Service and rangers ever on the alert for any appearance of smoke or steam, it is not probable that a destructive eruption would occur, even in our volcanic belt, without due warning to the people of the vicinity. The conversion of areas around active volcanoes into national parks (as in Alaska, Hawaii, California, Oregon, Idaho, etc.) also provides watchful protection as well as opportunities to observe volcanoes from a safe distance.

An Afterthought

There are hundreds of volcanoes in the world that have not been mentioned in these pages, for no attempt has been made to cover the field completely. Only those volcanoes that have been of special interest to the writer, and that seem to have interested other people also, are here discussed. But in numberless places—in the Pacific Ocean, in the Atlantic and Indian Oceans; in Madagascar, the Canaries, and other islands off the coast of Africa; in Borneo and other islands of the South Seas; in Kamchatka, Persia, and other parts of Asia; all along the Andes and islands off the coast of South America—volcanoes continue to change the surface of the earth and the depth of the seas.

At the present writing, so far as we know, Parícutin is the youngest volcano in an inhabited country, and it has had more careful attention than any other volcano born in modern times. It may be that Parícutin is a more important volcano than some of us realize. It has awakened the interest of scientists, and made them conscious of the much neglected field of volcanology by offering them an opportunity to observe its growth and behavior from infancy to maturity.

Thirteen months after Parícutin's appearance an extraordinary eruption of Vesuvius, with British and American soldiers on the ground to add greater excitement to the event, provided further stimulation to scientific interest, as well as more data for the records. And this is important; for the study of volcanoes is the key which opens the way for geology, and for an understanding of the constitution of our earth.

With the timely impetus provided by Parícutin, it seems probable that from now on more rapid advancement than ever before

213

will be made (1) in the understanding of this forceful expression of Nature's energy, (2) in the protection of life and property from its ravages, and (3) in harnessing this heat and power in the service of man instead of leaving it to wasteful destruction.

Already some thought has been given to the problem of protection from lava flows in Hawaii and Sicily, by building strong embankments to divert future lava flows into unproductive areas. For more than a hundred years the fumeroles of Tuscany have been utilized to recover the boric acid which they bring up from below, and for a long time sulphur has been collected from various craters of the world. In recent years, much heat from geysers and fumeroles has been utilized by man. The fumerole field north of Rome has been developed with powerhouses that supply electricity to several cities. In California wells have been drilled in fumerole areas in order to bring up superheated steam under controlled conditions.

But these are only beginnings. The human intelligence which has harnessed so much of electrical power, controlled so much water power, brought radium out of the earth and violet rays out of the sun, has even split the atom and begun to learn to control the terrific energy thus released, will certainly learn, in time, to direct the heat, the gases, and other chemicals of erupting volcanoes into many other channels that serve the needs of man.

References for Further Reading

Ball, Sir Robert S., *The Earth's Beginnings*, D. Appleton, 1902.

Barns, Thomas A., *Across the Great Craterland to the Congo*, E. Benn, Ltd., 1923.

Bonney, T. G., *The Structure of the Earth*, T. C. and E. C. Jack, 1912.

Bowden, Arthur T., *Man's Physical Universe*, The Macmillan Co., 1943.

Cressy, George B., *Asia's Land and Peoples*, McGraw-Hill Book Co., Inc., 1944.

Day, Arthur L., *Some Causes of Volcanic Activity*, The Franklin Institute, 1924; *Volcanic Activity and Hot Springs of Lassen Peak*, Carnegie Institution of Washington, Pub. No. 360, 1925.

Diller, J. S., *Lassen Peak, Our Most Active Volcano*, Seismological Society of America bulletin, Stanford Univ., 1916.

Fenton, Carroll Lane, *Earth's Adventures*, The John Day Co., 1942; *Our Amazing Earth*, Doubleday, Doran and Co., 1938.

Fenton and Fenton, *The Rock Book*, Doubleday, Doran and Co., 1940.

Heilprin, Angelo, *The Tower of Pelée*, J. B. Lippincott Co., 1904.

Houston, Edwin J., *Wonder Book of Volcanoes and Earthquakes*, Frederick A. Stokes, 1907.

Johnson, Gaylord, *Story of Earthquakes and Volcanoes*, Julian Messner Inc., 1938.

Johnson, George R., *Peru from the Air*, American Geographical Society, 1930.

Light, Richard Upton, *Focus on Africa*, American Geographical Society, 1941.

Life Magazine for April 17, 1944.

Longwell, Knopf, and Flint, *Outlines of Physical Geology*, John Wiley and Sons, 1941.

Morris, Charles, *The Volcano's Deadly Work*, W. E. Scull, 1902.

National Geographic Magazine, Jan., 1917, "Valley of Ten Thousand Smokes"; Feb., 1918, "Valley of Ten Thousand Smokes"; July, 1921, "Geography of Japan"; Sept., 1921, "Alaska, Our Greatest National Monument"; Feb., 1924, "Hawaii: America's Strongest Outpost of Defense"; March, 1924, "Among the Craters of the Moon"; April, 1924, "Sakurajima, Japan's Greatest Volcanic Eruption"; Jan., 1929, "Bogosloff"; March, 1937, "Crater Lake and Yosemite Through the Ages"; Oct., 1938, "Hawaii Then and Now"; Oct., 1939, "Living on an Active Volcano"; July, 1941, "Chile's Land of Fire and Water"; Dec., 1941, "From Sea to Clouds in Ecuador"; Feb., 1944, "Parícutin, the Cornfield that Grew a Volcano"; Aug., 1944, "Nicaragua, a Land of Lakes and Volcanoes"; Nov., 1944, "Coffee is King in El Salvador."

National Research Council, Bulletin No. 77 (*Vulcanology*), 1931.

Natural History Magazine, Nov., 1942, "The Devil's Tower"; Oct., 1943, "Parícutin is Born"; Oct., 1944, "Parícutin Comes of Age."

Pan American Magazine, Oct., 1943, "The Birth of a Volcano"; July-Sept., 1943, "The Most Volcanic America."

Perret, Frank A., *The Eruption of Mt. Pelée*, Carnegie Institution of Washington Publication No. 458, 1935.

Russell, Israel C., *Volcanoes of North America*, The Macmillan Co., 1897.

Squier, E. G., *The Volcanoes of Central America and the Geographical and Topographical Features of Nicaragua, as Connected with the Proposed Inter-Oceanic Canal*, New Haven, 1850.

Volcano Letter (quarterly published by the University of Hawaii), all issues, especially during 1931.

Williams, Howel, *Crater Lake; the Story of Its Origin*, University of California Press, 1941.

Index

(Note: Names of volcanoes are in boldface type)

217

218

219

221

222

QE
522
C5
Coleman
Volcanoes new and old

Glen Oaks Community College
Library
Centreville, Michigan